The Italian Influence on
English Barometers from 1780

The Italian Influence on
English Barometers from 1780

Edwin Banfield

Baros Books

First published 1993

Baros Books
5 Victoria Road
Trowbridge
Wiltshire
BA14 7LH

British Library Cataloguing-in-publication Data
A catalogue record for this book is available from the British Library

ISBN 0-948382-07-4

Cover illustration: Diorama showing Torricelli's barometer experiment (*The Science Museum, London*)

Typesetting by Ex Libris Press, 1 The Shambles, Bradford-on-Avon, Wiltshire

Illustrations screened by Norton Photo Litho, New Pitt Cottages, Paulton

Printed and bound in Great Britain by Dotesios Ltd, Trowbridge, Wiltshire

Contents

Preface

The barometer was invented in 1643 by an Italian, Evangelista Torricelli, so it is not surprising that Italians have had a considerable influence on its development and design. What is perhaps surprising is that by 1800 Italian barometer makers and retailers should have dominated the market in domestic barometers in Britain.

The Italian climate meant that there was little demand for barometers at home; and this, coupled with adverse living conditions in northern Italy towards the end of the eighteenth century, forced the majority of Italian barometer makers to seek a better living selling them in northern Europe, particularly in France, The Netherlands and Britain.

The vast majority of barometers made in Britain before about 1800 were of the stick or cistern tube type. Hooke's innovative wheel mechanism had not been received enthusiastically in Britain and very few were made in the seventeenth and eighteenth centuries: the wheel instrument was regarded as too expensive and not as accurate as the cistern tube type.

All this changed when the Italian barometer makers began to settle in Britain towards the end of the eighteenth century. They introduced their version of the wheel barometer, which became known as the banjo barometer because its shape was similar to the banjo musical instrument. They were cheap and attractive barometers and soon became very much in demand throughout Britain.

This book is not intended to be a history of the barometer, although it does contain information on changes to its style and design. A concise history of the development of the barometer can be found in my *Antique Barometers: an Illustrated Survey*; for a more comprehensive guide, see my three companion volumes: *Barometers: Stick or Cistern Tube, Barometers: Wheel or Banjo* and *Barometers: Aneroid and Barographs*.

Research for my previous book, *Barometer Makers and Retailers 1660–1900* disclosed a surprising number of Italian names, which prompted me to look into the reasons for this. This book is the result of this enquiry.

Acknowledgements

I am very grateful to all those who have provided photographs for this book, which are acknowledged in the captions.
I would also like to thank the following for all the help that they have given me:

Paolo Brenni of Paris for bringing to my attention the article 'I Baromèta del Lago di Como' by Venosto Lucati on the Italian background.

Maxwell Craven, Keeper of Antiquities at the City of Derby Museum and Art Gallery, for material on the Bregazzi family.

David Day of Negretti Automation, Aylesbury for making available the early records of the Negretti & Zambra partnership.

Dario A. Fumolo and John Forster, both of London, for material on London barometer makers.

Mr E.W. Richards of Bromley for illustrations of barometers.

Barbara Ronchetti of Worcester and Jenny Wetton, Curator of Science at the Museum of Science and Industry, Manchester, for information on barometer makers in the Manchester area.

Hugh H. Watson of Grantham for information on barometer makers in Lincolnshire, particularly the Bellatti family.

Thanks also to my daughter, Sue Ashton, for editing the manuscript.

Fig. 1   Lake Como, Lombardy, Italy, c.1830.

Fig. 2   St Gotthard Pass, Switzerland.

1

The Italian Background

The Italian contribution to scientific knowledge has been considerable. The universities of Padua, Bologna and Pisa were of the greatest importance in the revival of scientific studies in the sixteenth and seventeenth centuries, and drew to Italy a host of foreign scholars, including Copernicus, Vesalius and William Harvey, who discovered the circulation of the blood. Galileo Galilei (1564–1642) was appointed to the chair of mathematics at Pisa when he was only twenty-three, and in 1612 he made his improved thermometer. One of his pupils, Torricelli, invented the barometer, which Viviani constructed in 1643.

Italian craftsmen seem to have been quick to reproduce and popularise the inventions of the scientific scholars. According to Giambattista Giovio, in a commentary of around 1770:

> Scarcely had the immortal Galileo in Venice observed the secrets of the heavens with the telescope, than our Lariani [inhabitants of the Lake Como region] constructed them throughout Europe. Scarcely had Torricelli in Tuscany measured the degrees of heat in the atmosphere with the thermometer, and variations in its weight with the barometer, than they [the Lariani] duplicated these instruments in every far flung country, and then they return joyfully to their families and their fecund wives with whom we see them gathering the grape harvest.

Giovio refers specifically to the inhabitants of the mountainous area around Lake Como in Lombardy, an area famed for its beauty and dramatic views (*Fig.* 1). It was a favourite haunt of English Romantic poets Shelley and Wordsworth and a source of inspiration to nineteenth-century composers, including Verdi, Bellini, Liszt and Rossini. The French writer Stendhal found Como 'the most beautiful place in the world'. The lake is over thirty miles long and up to two and three-quarter miles wide. It was named Lacus Larius by the Romans and is still sometimes referred to as Lago Lario.

The inhabitants of the region were mainly farmers, but as there was very little to do on the land during the long winter months the farmers and their sons tended to engage in such crafts as silk weaving, wood carving and instrument making. Many of the Catholic families were large, and the income from the land was not sufficient to support them all year round, so that it was essential to supplement their income by these secondary pursuits. Demand for their goods was limited in northern Italy so that they had to travel north to Switzerland and beyond in order to sell them. Giovio goes on to describe this activity:

Around Lake Como is to be found the most ingenious and industrious district perhaps in Europe. From no area, with such narrow confines, are sent elsewhere – to Spain, Portugal, Germany, France, Sicily – so many colonies; and if from one place go artificers and traders, from the next go electrical machines, barometers, telescopes and physics experimenters.

It is difficult to establish when the workers in the Lake Como area first began to make barometers, but there is evidence that barometers were being made at least by 1745. Count Alessandro Volta, the famous Italian physicist, was born in Brunate, a village a little east of Como, in 1745; we know that his nurse Elisabetta was the wife of Lodovico Monti, a barometer maker. In 1787, Giovio defended the population of the Como area, who were 'compelled by poverty to scatter themselves all over Europe, trading and earning profits; if this trading did not assist the poverty of the countryside, I would fear the agriculture of the mountains would also decay.' In a pamphlet proposing the setting up of a market in Como to encourage trade, he states that the 79,838 inhabitants of the province can survive for only eight months of the year on farming income alone.

In 1774 Councillor Guiseppe Pecis, Superintendant General of Roads and Water for the Government of Milan, wrote a report on the Lake Como region in connection with a scheme to make the River Adda navigable. His report included the following description of the inhabitants of the area:

> They are those who travel through every nation carrying for sale barometers, thermometers, optical implements and various other things of a similar kind. There is no district around the lake, and the Valassina [just east of Lake Como] which has not a number of such people. Many of those who have come back always go to Como and by the appearance and fashion of their dress it is easy to know from which country they are returning. They begin by selling barometers and then confine themselves to one or other kind of portable merchandise. It is their custom to set out at an early age, following friends or relatives already used to travel. Sometimes they return after a few years, then set off again; others remain far from home until the age to marry. Then they stay home for a few years and later set off again on their travels. Generally, they all return with money and some have done extremely well.

Venosto Lucati, in an article on the barometer makers of the Lake Como region, attributes the emigration or 'travels' of the local people to grave economic circumstances and to excessive taxation, particularly harsh in the Lake Como area during the seventeenth and eighteenth centuries. Although the economy revived towards the end of the eighteenth century, emigration continued because of the concomitant rise in the population.

Conditions in eighteenth-century Italy were unstable; the country was divided and ruled by foreign kings, the Church was not sympathetic to the new learning and poverty was widespread. Families were large, with the result that some ambitious and enterprising young men in the north of Italy crossed the Alps to Switzerland and went on to settle in France, The Netherlands, Austria and Germany. Some made their way to Britain and among them were barometer makers who started small businesses, often with like-minded compatriots.

In April 1796 the French armies of Napoleon invaded northern Italy and by 1799 had conquered the whole mainland. Apart from a few months, they remained in control, until 1814, of the whole peninsula except for Venetia, the area around Venice, which had been given to Austria. The French occupation had far-reaching effects on Italy; the power of the Church and of the Pope was reduced and a new middle class began to appear. Changes were made in land ownership and some was redistributed. Agriculture was improved and the peasants were freed from their old feudal ties and obligations. But the French did not want competition from Italian manufactured goods; they just wanted Italian raw materials, such as silk, for their own home industries; so Italian industry remained undeveloped.

Conscription of Italians into the Napoleonic armies was introduced, and by 1812 no less than 91,000 had been recruited. In the Peninsular and Russian campaigns, Italian losses were 22,000 and 26,000 respectively. As a result, between 1800 and 1815, many Italians left Italy in order to avoid conscription and the wars being waged by Napoleon. Those who went north to Switzerland had to make the arduous and dangerous journey over the St Gotthard Pass (*Fig.* 2) where some lost their lives. In 1805 Napoleon opened up the Simplon Pass which made travel to northern Europe much easier.

Lady Morgan, writing about Italy in 1821, commented that the population of several villages near the lakes appeared to consist only of women.

These poor men of Comaschi [Lake Como], driven by the necessities of life, have been emigrating from time immemorial into almost all countries ... in order to devote themselves to petty commerce which they pursue industriously as well as frugally. It is they who can be met everywhere with barometers, mirrors, coloured prints, gilt picture frames and other objects produced by the industry of their native land. And then when they have managed to put together enough money, they cheerfully abandon the streets of Paris, London, Madrid, and return to their native solitudes, which for them is always the land of Canaan. They do not always make a fortune, but sometimes it happens that they return well enough provided with means to acquire the very lands they had once tilled, and they spend liberally the money they brought in abundance from beyond the Alps.

Writing in 1817, Carlo Amoretti observed:

These highlanders [from Lake Como] are accustomed to going elsewhere to sell their wares, and it is apt to say that they are most ingenious, since generally it is they who construct the barometers, thermometers and other physics instruments, even those new to general use, as they come to be invented. Circumstances compel them to take with them other goods. Then they return home every two years to spend their earnings made abroad on the acquisition of land, or on the improvement of what they already possess. Scarcely a tenth of the men do not emigrate.

Venosto Lucati also gives the opinion that the wandering pedlars were not merely sellers of their wares, but also the makers:

Fig. 4   Barometer pedlar in Germany.

GRAHMED EN GUTE BAROMETER!

Wer sich nicht wol versteht aufs wetter,
Der brauchet einen Barometer.

Fig. 3   Barometer pedlar in Switzerland.

These small scientific instruments, beginning with the barometers which they carried everywhere, were the product of their own hard work. They were typical artisans who, by their firesides in the desolate months of winter, put their talents to the manufacture of those objects which still arouse a certain wonder in the regions beyond the Alps.

The Italians of the Lake Como area must have been an exceptional people, possessing great courage, energy and initiative. There were no formal apprenticeships, but the father passed on his barometer making knowledge to his son, cousin or nephew and there were also many alliances between families through marriage.

By the end of the seventeenth century in France, barometers and thermometers were being produced by craftsmen; they were often made by enamellers because the graduated scale was inscribed on an enamel plate. Hubin, one of the first to produce these instruments for commercial use, was an enameller. These craftsmen adopted the title of 'physicist' and made various instruments such as electric machines and air pumps.

During the third quarter of the eighteenth century in France, barometers and thermometers became popular as domestic instruments and they were sold by Italians in the streets, promenades and cafés in Paris and in other towns and cities in France. Italian names on French barometers include Francis Molti, Jean Primavesy, Casati, Betalli, Casartelli, Polti, Torre and C. Ciceri & Cie who, like other Italians, also sold instruments by British makers.

In the second half of the eighteenth century, quite a number of Italians settled in The Netherlands and worked as barometer, thermometer and cabinet makers, glassblowers and plasterers. Their route from Italy was probably by mule or dog cart across the Alps and then by boat across the Boden lake and down the Rhine to Amsterdam.

There is evidence that Italian pedlars and hawkers were active in The Hague as early as 1710, and from 1740 onwards they frequented Amsterdam, Groningen, Haarlem, Rotterdam and other towns (*Figs* 3 and 4). Some makers travelled from town to town selling barometers and other instruments from a room in an inn or a stall at a market or fair. Some of the barometer dials were engraved with bilingual weather indications such as Latin and Dutch, French or German.

In the *Rotterdam Courier* of 1749, Antonio Formentino and Antonio Reballio advertised for sale 'wheel barometers, thermometers and a barometer working like a clock'. Around 1750, Antonio Ciquino was using a trade card printed in Dutch which read 'Makes, sells and repairs all kinds of barometers and thermometers, sells also a great variety of field-glasses, and glasses for optical instruments at moderate prices.' His trade card was affixed to the box of a Culpeper microscope constructed by John Uring of 174 Fenchurch Street, London, which suggests that Ciquino also imported and sold British instruments.

Italian names found on Dutch barometers made during the second half of the eighteenth century include Frans Primavesi, Peter Poleti, J. Molteni, Bianchi, Poletta Gilardoni, Bazzerga and J. Solaro. Italian names on Dutch barometers made during the first half of the nineteenth century include Joseph Pagani, G. Bernasconi, D. Barella, D. Sala, J. Stoppani, J.M. Tognia, Grimoldi and A. Solaro who was in partnership with Donato Butti who came from Milan.

2

Early Italian Migrants to Britain

Of the many Italians who touted their barometers around Europe during the eighteenth century, only a comparative few reached as far north as Britain. Italian acrobats, street musicians and strolling artists had been seen in Britain from at least the beginning of the eighteenth century, but it was not until the last quarter of the century that skilled craftsmen began to appear in any number: these were mainly barometer, thermometer, looking-glass, picture frame and bird cage makers; also carvers, gilders, silverers, wire workers and cabinet makers.

It is difficult to trace the early Italian barometer makers who arrived in Britain before 1800 as very few of them appear in the Post Office directories, rate or parish records. The early directories did not classify traders by their trades, which makes looking for them very difficult, particularly if the surname was mis-spelt. The Post Office directories of London in 1810 record only four Italian barometer and thermometer makers, four looking-glass makers and silverers, one carver, gilder and cabinet maker and one picture, looking-glass and frame maker. It is known, from extant barometers, that there were many more Italians making barometers in London during the first decade of the nineteenth century than those recorded. Some of these were no doubt itinerant workers who returned to Italy from time to time and this probably explains why some early barometers, made around 1800, are engraved with the name of the maker but bear no address.

By the end of the eighteenth century, Britain had become a prosperous country and barometers were becoming fashionable and popular instruments among the growing numbers of middle-class families and were purchased as a status symbol. The rapidly expanding market in barometers attracted the Italians who had long experience in glassblowing, carving, gilding and frame making.

The Italian artisan workers settled mainly in the Holborn area of London; it was situated conveniently between the City and the West End, rents of the lodging houses were very cheap and related crafts, such as clock and precision instrument making, were already established there. Once a nucleus of Italians had settled in the area, it had the effect of attracting further Italian migrants, often relatives, with the result that the area later became known as 'Little Italy'. It comprised a rectangular area bounded by Gray's Inn Road on the west, Holborn on the south, Farringdon on the east and Rosebury Avenue on the north side.

The area was shared with unskilled Italian workers such as organ grinders, street musicians, figure sellers and, later, ice cream vendors. These workers lived mainly in Summer Street, Eyre Street Hill and Saffron Hill, which was a poor area, while the skilled workers occupied better quality houses in Hatton Garden, Hatton Wall, Leather Lane, Cross Street, Charles Street, Dorrington Street, Baldwins Gardens, Grenville Street and Holborn Hill.

Some barometer makers lived alone, but others shared a house with one or more other makers. Also resident were apprentices, servants and pedlars of barometers. The address 81 Holborn, 81 High Holborn or 81 Holborn Hill appears to have been used by various Italians when they first arrived in London before they became settled and established and able to find individual premises from which to trade. It is known to have been used by James Lione, Dominick Lione, Joseph Somalvico, J. Cetti and Cattely & Co. James Lione seems to have been the only maker who remained at the address for any length of time and he could well have rented or owned it.

It seems that very few Italian women accompanied the men to Britain, with the result that most men married English women, although a few returned to Italy to find a wife. The majority of young men came from Italy to be apprenticed to a relative already in Britain or to a maker who came from the same village in the Lake Como area and was known to the apprentice's family. In 1851, 506 Italian men and 20 Italian women were recorded in the Holborn area; of the men, only 94 were married and of these only ten had Italian wives; 74 had English wives, five had Irish wives and five had wives of other nationalities.

The young Italians had a reputation for hard work and for living life to the full. The author of an article on 'The Italians in Hatton Garden' in *The Holborn and Bloomsbury Journal* in 1866 wrote that 'The first great resort of the Italians was the public house or coffee shop, the second the barber's, and the third the church.' High-spirited young glassblowers had a reputation for working late into the night to make up for time lost after weekends of excessive drinking! It was nevertheless claimed that a very efficient worker could produce up to 18 dozen thermometers a week.

The Italians were Catholics and the early migrants attended the local Sardinian Chapel, which was the oldest Roman Catholic centre in London. Later, in 1864, St Peter's Church was completed in Hatton Garden to provide for the increase in the Italian population of the area. It was noted that the young men attended church wearing brigand hats, black capes and peg-top trousers, while the older men wore Garibaldi cloaks with astrakhan collars, silver buckles and clasps. The women wore long full dresses with brightly coloured head-dresses and shawls. Their houses were decorated in Italian style, with souvenirs and pictures of Italy, trinkets and small straw-plaited baskets decorated with raised flowers. Celebrations and festivals were accompanied by the sound of the mandolin and accordian.

The design and construction of the great majority of barometers bearing Italian names and addresses from all over Britain are remarkably uniform, which suggests that the cases at least were made in quantity by a few specialist case makers. There also appears to be little variation in design on a regional basis and there is evidence to suggest that the barometer makers in London used pedlars or hawkers to sell their barometers around the country, while makers who settled in cities and towns around Britain purchased complete barometers or their individual parts from the London makers. The records of the partnership of Negretti & Zambra show the extent to which they supplied Italian and English makers, both within and outside London (see chapter 6).

William Lacy was a barometer frame maker at West Street, West Smithfield, London and his signature appears on the back of many cases made between about 1810 and 1840. The dials or spirit level plates of these barometers are signed by London and provincial makers, which suggests that many makers around the country looked to London for their cases or complete barometers. Similarly, Richard & Henry Frankham were engravers at 15 Wilson Street, Gray's Inn Road, London from 1829 to 1855 when the firm became Frankham & Wilson until 1870. The reverse side of many register plates and dials are signed by the Frankhams, while the names engraved on the front of the plates and dials are London and provincial makers. It is known that barometers made by the Ronchettis of Manchester were engraved by the Frankhams which indicates that they purchased their barometers, or at least the various parts, in London.

It is, in any case, difficult to establish who actually made a particular barometer. Some makers made the complete instrument; others made some parts and bought in the rest, while some bought all the parts, including the case, and then assembled them. The remainder, who should be described as retailers, bought barometers from wholesalers and had their names engraved on the dial or level plate. Some makers advertised barometers for sale 'wholesale or retail', and were keen to increase their sales by selling wholesale to various retailers.

James Peote, an Italian weather-glass maker, was one of the early migrants to move out of London. In May 1792 he used the local paper to 'inform his Friends, that he has taken a house in Boston, Lincolnshire where he makes and sells all sorts of Barometers and Thermometers, for Brewers, Distillers etc.' In July, he announced that he was from 94 Holborn Hill, London and 'Respectfully informs his Friends, and the Public in general, that he has taken a House, and fitted up a Shop in the Angel Lane, Boston where he makes and repairs all Sorts of Single Barometers, Double Ditto, Portable Ditto, and Angle Ditto; Thermometers for Brewers and Distillers.' By October that year Peote was advertising again:

Having taken and entered upon a new Shop in Mr. Damant's Street, adjoining Strait-Bargate, Boston, begs leaves to inform the Ladies, Gentlemen and Public in general, he has just arrived from London with a large Assortment of Barometers of different sorts; particularly the Wheel Thermometers and Barometers, for Physicians, Philosophers etc. N.B. Articles may be had Wholesale or Retail, on the most moderate terms, and if not approved, may be returned or changed; assuring them that every Endeavour in his Power will be exerted to merit their Favours, and gratefully acknowledged.

Louis Bellatti, in Grantham, Lincolnshire, also advertised that he was supplied from London. In April 1819 he announced that he had 'formed a connection in London from whence he is supplied with every article in his line of the very best quality; and begs to inform the nobility and gentry, that he will attend at their houses for the purpose of repairing Barometers, Thermometers and Optical Instruments of every description.'

Other London makers used agents to take their barometers into the provinces for sale. Joseph Cesare Zambra began his career as an itinerant salesman, selling an assortment of jewellery, small cutlery, watches, barometers and thermometers. He came to London around 1816 from Careno on Lake Como and was first employed by Joseph Cetti of London, who also originated from Careno. Facilities for travelling were limited in the early eighteenth century, so the young men generally undertook their journeys on foot, taking a particular district or county and returning to London at the end of the month. Zambra's area covered parts of Essex where he met, and later married, Phillis Warren of Saffron Walden (see chapter 6).

Zambra acted as an agent for Cetti; other travellers and hawkers purchased their barometers and other wares from the makers or retailers, and carried them with them on foot, by barrow, on horseback or by horsedrawn vehicle. They were disliked by other retailers as they could undercut prices due to their very low overheads. In 1823 a Society for the Protection of Trade was established to enforce the law against persons who hawked manufactured goods from door to door without a licence. The *Manchester Guardian* records in 1823 that the Manchester Trade Society took a Joanno Cocina to court for hawking pictures, looking-glasses, barometers and other goods in Ardwick. The defence claimed that he was working for Antonio Peduzzi, who had two shops in the city, but he was fined £10 or three months in prison. The fine was not paid so he served the prison sentence.

Makers, of course, sometimes did their own hawking. In Scotland, George Lowden (1825–1912), an optician and scientist, wrote in his autobiography:

There was when I commenced business no regular manufacturing optician in Dundee. One Balerno, who lived in Yeoman Shore, and another, Anthony Tarone, who had his house in Murraygate, gave themselves out as 'barometer and mirror makers'. The former hawked his goods about the street, and usually had a barometer under one arm. Hawking was then in great vogue.

Anthony Tarone was working in Dundee from 1818 to 1843; Domenico Balerno was there between 1846 and 1853.

Although the majority of itinerant vendors travelled on foot, it seems that they covered the whole country. Throughout the nineteenth century methods of transport improved; there were canals and rivers for transporting goods, and coach services ran regularly to all the large towns. The Royal London Mail Coach took only 28 hours to travel from London to Manchester, and in 1825 the first working railway opened between Stockton and Darlington. During the following 12 years, some 1,500 miles of track were laid in the United Kingdom and by 1885 the length of track had increased to 16,700 miles.

George Borrow, in his book *Wild Wales*, published in 1862, tells of an encounter with an Italian traveller on a journey in Wales in 1854 that took place at The Lion Inn at Cerrig y Drudion between Llangollen and Bangor. He describes the Italian:

He was a short, thick, strongly-built fellow of about thirty-seven with a swarthy face, raven black hair, high forehead and dark deep eyes, full of intelligence and great determination. He was dressed in a velveteen coat with broad lappets, red waistcoat, velveteen breeches buttoning a little way below the knee; white stockings apparently of lamb's wool and high-lows.

'Pray speak a little Italian to him', said the good landlady to me.

'From the Lago di Como?' said I, trying to speak Italian.

'Si signore, but how came you to think that I was from the Lake of Como?'

'Because', said I, 'when I was a ragazzo I knew many from the Lake of Como, who dressed much like yourself. They wandered about the country with boxes on their backs and weather-glasses in their hands, but had their head-quarters at Norwich where I lived.'

'Do you remember any of their names?' said the Italian.

'Giovanni Gestra and Luigi Pozzi', I replied.

'I have seen Giovanni Gestra myself', said the Italian, 'and I have heard of Luigi Pozzi. Gestra has returned to the Lago, but no one knows what is become of Pozzi.'

'The last time I saw him', I said, 'was about eighteen years ago at Corunna in Spain; he was then in a sad drooping condition and said he bitterly repented ever quitting Norwich.'

'E con ragione', said the Italian, 'for there is no place like Norwich for doing business in the world. I myself have sold seventy pounds' worth of weather-glasses at Norwich in one day. One of our people is living there now who has done bene, molto bene.'

'You speak English remarkably well', said I; 'have you been long in Britain?'

'I came over about four years ago', said the Italian.

'On your own account?' said I.

'Not exactly, signore; my brother, who was in business in Liverpool, wrote to me to come over to assist him. I did so, but soon left him, and took a shop for myself at Denbigh, where, however, I did not stay long. At present I travel for an Italian house in London, spending the summer in Wales and the winter in England.'

'And what do you sell?' said I.

'Weather-glasses, signore, pictures and little trinkets such as country people like.'

By 1850 the artisan firms recorded with Italian names in the London Post Office directories were 21 barometer and thermometer makers, 25 looking-glass makers and silverers, nine carvers and gilders and cabinet makers, eight picture and looking-glass frame makers and five wire workers and bird cage makers. There was a loose connection between these artisan trades as a third of the barometer and thermometer makers recorded were also noted as looking-glass makers. These artisans had similar regional backgrounds and were emigrants from Piedmont, Lombardy and Liguria where there was a long-standing tradition of craftsmanship in precision and musical instruments, although the barometer makers came almost exclusively from the Como area.

Giovanni Battista Torre was probably the first Italian barometer maker to start trading in London. In 1760, he opened a shop in Paris to sell scientific instruments, including barometers, and in 1767 he opened a London branch in Pall Mall which was managed by his son Anthony. Giovanni died in 1780 and the firm became Torre Brothers in 1783. Paul Colnaghi joined the business in 1785 and eventually traded as fine art dealers under the name of P.D. Colnaghi. Torre made stick, wheel and double barometers.

Christopher Bettally also had a shop in Paris before working in Pimlico and then Oxford Street, London between 1787 and 1793. His trade card (*Fig. 5*) shows him to have been a 'Constructor of all sorts of Barometers, Thermometers, Hygrometers and all sorts of Phisical Instruments of Glass'. A barometer that can be attributed to him is illustrated in *Fig.* 7. The case is veneered in mahogany with satinwood crossbanding and marquetry decoration. The oat-beard hygrometer has a mahogany bezel with a flat glass and this is repeated for the main dial, where the bezel is hinged and locked with a key. The silvered brass dial has a blued steel indicating hand and a brass recording hand which is operated by a pulley mechanism from the ivory key above the bezel. The case is surmounted by a scroll pediment with a brass finial and the overall height is 38 inches.

Some of the Italian surnames on barometers made in France and Holland are identical or similar to surnames on barometers made in Britain, but there is no evidence to suggest that barometer makers who had established themselves in France or Holland later moved on to Britain, or that a reverse movement occurred. It is known that at least two makers had shops in both London and Paris (Torre and Bettally as mentioned above), but it appears that members of the same family settled in more than one country and that they visited each other from time to time.

While Italians were arriving in London between 1790 and 1820, a similar migration, but on a much smaller scale, was taking place to Manchester. Merchants had been coming to Manchester from Italy to buy wool and woollen cloth from as early as the Middle Ages, so the city was well known to the Italians. There was a rapid growth in business and industry in the city in the late eighteenth and early nineteenth centuries, and the increased wealth created resulted in a rapid growth in the population.

Reviewing the history of Manchester in the *Manchester Guardian* in 1894, a journalist commented 'For some reason there was a remarkable influx of Italians into Manchester about 1810 including Zanettis, Bolongaros, Casartellis, Ronchettis, Peduzzis, Bianchis and others who were carvers, gilders, picture dealers, makers of barometers and thermometers and of plaster casts.' J.T. Slugg also wrote of the Italian immigration;

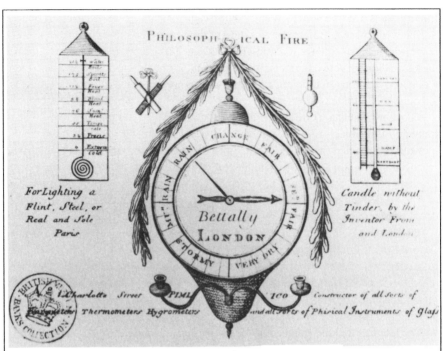

Fig. 5 Trade card of C. Bettally, c.1790 (*Trustees of the British Museum*).

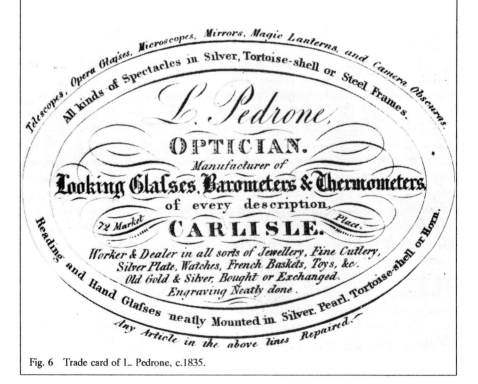

Fig. 6 Trade card of L. Pedrone, c.1835.

Fig. 7   Mahogany 12 inch barometer attributed to C. Bettally, c.1790.

in a letter in 1874 to the *Manchester Guardian* he wrote: 'I came to Manchester and lived in Market Street as an apprentice in 1829 ... Several natives of Italy, principally from the neighbourhood of Lake Como, had established themselves in Manchester as shopkeepers.' In his *Reminiscences of Manchester Fifty Years Ago*, published in 1881, he wrote:

> Fifty years ago several respectable Italians were in business here as carvers and gilders, looking-glass makers and printsellers ... Joshua Ronchetti was a noted maker of barometers, thermometers and specially hydrometers ... His son-in-law, Mr Casartelli, succeeded him and occupied the same premises. Baptist, the father of Joshua Ronchetti, was a 'weather-glass maker' in High Street. Joshua had two sons, Baptist and Joshua, who followed the same business in London.

The lifestyle of the Italians in Manchester was similar to that of the Italians in London. Isobel Banks, a Manchester novelist, recorded that in the 1820s it was the custom for house owners and shopkeepers to sublet their basements to craftsmen, including barometer makers, as workshops or for the sale of their goods. The Italians who were able to own or rent houses converted them into business premises with a workshop in the basement. Others had their workshops in sheds behind the houses and shops. In the 1830s Dominic Bolongaro, Joseph Marone and Vincent Zanetti all had shops in Market Street and frequented The Fox public house, run by Mrs Elizabeth Lax, a popular landlady on Cockpit Hill.

Anthony Peduzzi was a well-known barometer maker in Manchester. It is believed that he emigrated from Lombardy, Italy around 1810 and set up in Oldham Street. James Butterworth, in his *Antiquities of the Town and a Complete History of the Trade of Manchester*, published in 1822, describes Peduzzi's shop:

> A little lower down at No. 31 is the shop of Mr A. Peduzzi, carver, gilder, looking glass and picture frame maker, wholesale and retail. All kinds of needlework, drawings and pictures are elegantly framed and glazed by him, old frames and plates regilt or silvered, barometers, thermometers and hydrometers made and repaired.

It is said that he made well-finished and tastefully decorated instruments but that he spoke in very broken English. This is in contrast to Peter Pozzi, who was a barometer and looking-glass maker who was working in Willow Street, Oswestry at about the same time; it is said that he taught Italian in one lesson for one guinea.

As in London, not all the barometer makers were listed in the Manchester directories; the number of makers recorded in 1845 was only 13, and the figure was 14 in 1847 when the category was changed to mathematical and philosophical instrument maker, although opticians were entered separately.

In other parts of England, early recorded Italian barometer makers are George

Bianchi, Ipswich (1805), S. Bregazzi & Co., Derby (1809) and Peter A. Tarone, Bristol (1809). Italians appear to have settled in the larger towns and cities as glassblowers, carvers, gilders, opticians and barometer makers. Even in the small towns, barometers were sold engraved with Italian names, such as 'Catanio, Malton' and 'Pozzi, Wootton Bassett'. It is doubtful whether many of these Italians were actual makers, and it is more likely that they were shopkeepers and retailers who had their names engraved on the dials. There is a theory that some of the retailers were, in fact, Englishmen who arranged for Italian names to be engraved on their barometers because they were more popular and saleable than barometers bearing English names. It is also thought that some Italian makers, who were wholesalers, engraved their own names on the barometers but added the town or address of the retailer. This was certainly the practice of some clockmakers and it could account for the very large number of Italians who, on the face of it, appear to have been living in small towns throughout Britain.

The earliest Italian maker in Scotland appears to have been James Mariot; his address was Sign of the Crown, Gallowgate, Glasgow, and in the *Glasgow Journal* of 1742 he advertised that he came from Italy and sold 'All sorts of Barometers and Thermometers at the lowest prices ... He mends any old ones and exchanges new ones for old ones.' Another early Italian in Scotland was Charles Molinari, or Molinar as he was known in Edinburgh. He was born in Como, Italy and came to Edinburgh in 1752, working in the Netherbow as a barometer and philosophical glass maker who made stick and angle barometers. He also made double-angle barometers, similar to those made by Balthazar Knie and William Robb (see *Fig.* 8). These three makers appear to have been the only ones who made this type of instrument, the design of which seems to have originated in Germany. The double angle of the tube allows it to be housed on a symmetrical base and it was hoped that it would become a more popular item of furniture than the ordinary angle barometer which was shaped like a signpost. It had a bulb cistern tube which also originated on the Continent. It is not known whether it was Knie, Robb or Molinari who introduced this type of instrument to Scotland, but it never became popular.

Angelo Lovi, a glass manufacturer from Milan, came to Edinburgh in 1772 and worked in Niddry Street as a barometer and specific gravity bead maker; he made stick, wheel and double barometers similar to the one shown in *Fig.* 80 in chapter 4. Mrs Isobel Lovi, probably his widow, carried on the business from 1805 to 1827, and in 1805 patented an 'Apparatus for determining the specific gravity of fluid bodies'. This was used for precise measurements in industries as varied as bleaching and distilling. In 1813 she issued 'Directions for Using the Patent Areometric Beads'; these were part of the 'Apparatus' and were examined by T.C. Hope of the Highland Society for determining the richness of milk.

Another early migrant to Edinburgh was Antoni Galletti who set up in business as a barometer maker in 1798. He moved to Glasgow in 1805 and traded as an optical and mathematical instrument maker until 1850, when he was succeeded by his son John. They both sold 'Barometers and thermometers of all sorts, on the most approved principles'. John continued the business until he died in 1894. Another early maker

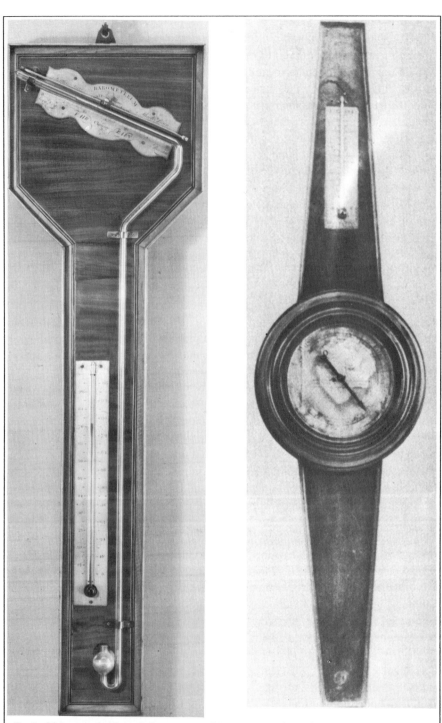

Fig. 8 Mahogany double-angle barometer, c.1790 (*Hotspur Ltd, London*).
Fig. 9 Mahogany wheel barometer by John Noseda, c.1790 (*Sotheby's, Sussex*).

in Glasgow was John Risso who is recorded in the first directory of 1783 as 'John Risso, makes thermometers, barometers etc. at Mr Stirlings, Surgeon, Saltmarket'.

There does not seem to be any evidence to suggest that there were any Italian barometer makers working in Wales during the eighteenth century, and only a few are recorded as working there in the first half of the nineteenth century. The reason is probably to be found in George Borrow's book, *Wild Wales*, quoted above. During a walk in 1854 from Llangollen to Bangor, Borrow stayed overnight at The Lion Inn at Cerrig y Drudion where he encountered an Italian who was travelling for an Italian house in London selling 'Weather glasses, pictures and little trinckets such as country people like'. Borrow asked if he sold many weather glasses in Wales, to which he replied: 'I do not, signore. The Welsh care not for weather glasses; my principal customers for weather glasses are the farmers of England.'

Of the few Italian makers operating from Wales in the early nineteenth century, the most prolific appears to have been the Maffia family in Monmouth who were watch, clock and barometer makers said to have come from Italy in 1841, although F.J. Britten in his *Old Clocks and Watches and their Makers* mentions a 'Watch 1798' by P. Maffia, Monmouth. Peter Maffia is recorded as working there from 1841 to 1871 and Dominic Maffia from 1868 to 1871, but they were also in partnership in 1868. Sheraton shell barometers signed P. Maffia & Co., Monmouth can be dated to about 1820, so it is quite likely that the family were in Monmouth from around 1800.

A comparatively small number of Italians emigrated to Ireland. Probably the first Belfast instrument maker was an Italian named John Noseda, who was a weather-glass maker who advertised in 1774 that he had 'Invented a kind of Balls for trying the Strength of Sour used for bleaching'. He died in 1779 and may well have been related to J. & P. Noseda of Walsall, England, who are known to have made Sheraton shell wheel barometers with shell and flower head paterae around 1820. The unusual straight-sided wheel instrument with a paper dial shown in *Fig.* 9 is signed 'John Noseda fecit'; as it has a wooden bezel it was probably made during the last quarter of the eighteenth century.

The first recorded Italian barometer maker to set up in business in Dublin was Andrew Gatty; he traded from 18 Fishamble in 1786 and moved to 1 Smock Alley in 1799. He was succeeded by Joseph Gatty at the same address in 1801 who remained there until 1814. Virtually all the Italians in Ireland were working in sea ports with easy access by sea to London or Liverpool, and it is not known how many of the barometer parts they made themselves or imported from their Italian relatives and friends in London. Some of them were carvers, gilders or glassblowers and acted as retailers for the London barometer wholesalers. Instruments were certainly imported from England to Ireland by the middle of the eighteenth century and these included barometers which became popular with amateur weather forecasters towards the end of the century.

3

Italian Influence on Style and Design

By the end of the eighteenth century Italian-made banjo barometers had completely ousted the English wheel barometer from the market and, during the first half of the nineteenth century, displaced the stick barometer in very many households. Very few wheel instruments made between 1780 and 1820 have English names. Those that did after 1800 were almost certainly made by Italians and retailed by the English, as they were identical to those made and sold by the Italians. Italian influence on the design and style of stick barometers was also significant.

Wheel or Banjo Barometers
Abraham Rees attributed the popularity of the wheel barometer to the Italians in his comments in *The Cyclopaedia* of 1819, though he was not impressed by the wheel barometer as a scientific instrument:

> The wheel barometer has lately obtruded on the public by strolling Italian hawkers in our streets, but the imperfect manner in which these barometers are executed, as well as their defective principle, renders them mere mechanical pictures, and not scientific instruments, in the parlour.

Despite the criticisms of Rees, the Italian supremacy continued well into the second half of the nineteenth century.

The wheel barometer, which was probably first made by Thomas Tompion, the famous clockmaker, to a design of Robert Hooke's in 1675, never laid claim to be as accurate as the stick barometer and was therefore not preferred as a scientific instrument. John Harris, in his *Lexicon Technicum* of 1704–10 described its sluggish mechanism:

> But this wheel barometer not answering fully the designed exactness, because the mercury is apt to stick about the sides of the glass, and would rise and fall by leaps, and all at once; and because also 'tis very difficult to adjust the ball and thread, etc. and that the instrument is very apt to be put out of order, etc. 'tis now out of use.

That it came back into fashion was largely due to the Italians.

Abraham Rees put his finger on it when he described wheel barometers as 'mere mechanical pictures ... in the parlour'. The wheel barometer became an attractive piece of furniture, rather than a scientific instrument, in the homes of the increasingly affluent middle classes. And its sluggish mechanism does have one advantage: tapping the glass has the effect of bringing the reading up to date, and the small adjustment seen in the indicating hand will show whether the pressure is rising or falling, and therefore provide an aid to weather forecasting.

How did the Italians succeed in popularising the wheel barometer? The answer appears to be by their hard work, aptitude, flair and ability in design and price competitiveness. In Italy and France during the second half of the eighteenth century the Italians were used to making banjo-shaped wheel barometers in the rococo style with lavish ornamentation of shell and scroll work, with the instrument usually carved and gilded (see *Figs* 10 and 11). They appear to have sensed that this design and decoration would not be popular in Britain, so they began to remodel the case, introducing simpler lines and decoration on the neo-classical style that had become popular under the lead of Robert Adam, the architect and furniture designer.

Impressed by the relics of the ancient world while studying in Italy from 1754 to 1758, Adam led the neo-classical revival when he set up an architectural practice in London with his three brothers on his return. The new designs were, in part, a reaction against the rococo style which had never been so wholeheartedly accepted in Britain as on the Continent. The Adams brothers decorated their furniture with delicate motifs, round and oval paterae, pendant husks, urns and fluting; line inlay and stringing and cross-banding were also employed. They also brought about a revival in fine inlay work, and marquetry came back into fashion using light-coloured woods such as satinwood and harewood, although mahogany was still favoured for veneers.

The Adams brothers employed at least four Italians to assist with the design and execution of their work. One was Michael Angelo Pergolesi, a designer and artist, who arrived in Britain in 1770 and published a series of *Original Designs* from 1777 for walls, ceilings, architraves, chimney pieces and furniture. Another was Giovanni Cipriani (1727–85), a Florentine artist and designer, who published a work on the *Rudiments of Drawing* in Britain between 1786 and 1792. These were engraved by Francesco Bartolozzi who came to England in 1764 and was a fellow pupil with Cipriani in Florence. Antonio Zucchi (1726–95) was a Venetian decorative painter; he met Maria Anna Angelica Kaufman, a Swiss painter and designer who was trained in Italy and was also working for the Adams brothers from 1765. They married and returned to Italy in 1781.

The Adams brothers were responsible for a formal style of decoration, and their style was popularised by later designers, particularly George Hepplewhite and Thomas Sheraton. Hepplewhite made use of oval and round paterae, swags, husks, flower and bell festoons, while Sheraton was noted for his shell inlay and thin stringing lines which he often used along the edges of his furniture.

It is reasonable to assume that the Italian migrant barometer makers, who arrived in England during the last quarter of the eighteenth century, consulted the Italians who

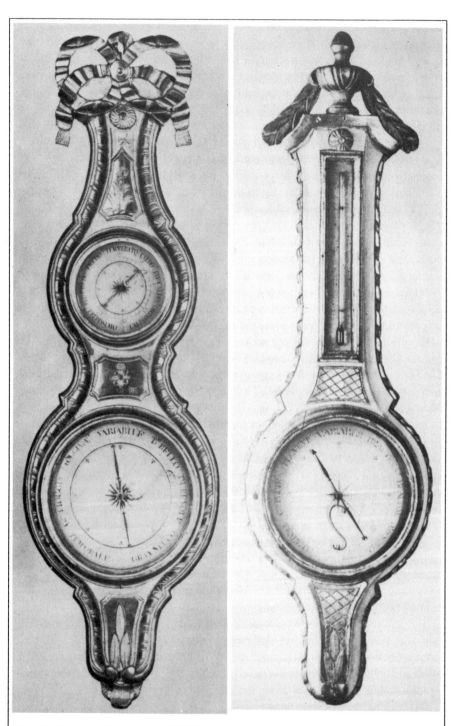

Fig. 10   Italian wheel barometer, c.1780 (*Institute and Museum of the History of Science, Florence*).
Fig. 11   French wheel barometer, c.1780 (*Lubeck Museum, Germany*).

were already here, particularly those working for the Adams brothers, as to the designs likely to be popular for barometer cases. They would have been influenced by the furniture being produced by the Adams brothers, and later by Hepplewhite and Sheraton. The Italians were quick to realise that by concealing the unattractive mercury tube within the wooden case and by using the float, pulley and dial method of recording air pressure, the position of the dial and form of the frame could be fashioned to suit changing tastes.

Much elegance of appearance and vitality could be given to the case, which was usually veneered with finely figured mahogany, or occasionally satinwood, and inlaid with the characteristic motifs of Hepplewhite and Sheraton. Outline stringing or cross-banding with contrasting woods was usual. Rosewood rather than mahogany appears to have been preferred by the Italians when decorating barometers with mother-of-pearl or brass inlay. This was because a greater contrast could be achieved by using rosewood as it was a darker wood. Two-line brass stringing was used to decorate some barometers; this was applied to outline the edges of the case and some had additional brass decoration above the main dial and round the set hand key.

The majority of wheel barometers in the last quarter of the eighteenth century had round tops, but occasionally scroll or broken pediments were used. *Fig.* 12 by Frans Pellegrino shows several features typical of an early Italian wheel barometer. The bezel extends almost to the edge of the case, it has a flat glass, and flowing lines which are gradually shaped. The dial inches are only graduated in tenths; twentieths are usual for early nineteenth-century instruments but later barometers are graduated to hundredths of an inch. The veneer around the sides of the case is laid across, rather than along, the length of the case; this also denotes quality.

A design of barometer case which became popular from around 1800 is shown in *Fig.* 13. The pine case is veneered with mahogany, outlined with chequered stringing and has marquetry inlay of two round and two oval fans. It has a broken pediment with a straight section or shoulder below it; this feature appeared on broken and scroll pediment barometers from around 1800 and its length was gradually extended until about 1820 (see *Fig.* 21 below). It is engraved J. Testi, Windmill, Leather Lane, Holborn, London and is very similar to the instrument shown in *Fig.* 14 by James Vechio, Dublin except that the Testi barometer has horizontal weather indications. Vechio was only described as a printseller and looking-glass manufacturer and it is highly likely that he bought the barometer in London with his name engraved on the dial.

The scroll or swan-necked pediment became more popular on wheel barometers from around 1805, but its use was generaly confined to barometers with 10 or 12 inch dials and it was not until around 1825 that the scroll pediment became the standard design for the vast majority of wheel barometers. A particularly elegant 10 inch dial barometer with scroll pediment by Charles Pitsalla, 221 High Holborn, London is illustrated in *Fig.* 15.

The case decoration of flower head and shell inlay became popular on wheel barometers around 1810, although this decoration had been used as early as 1795. The foliage, flower and shell motifs were derived from French decorative designs of around

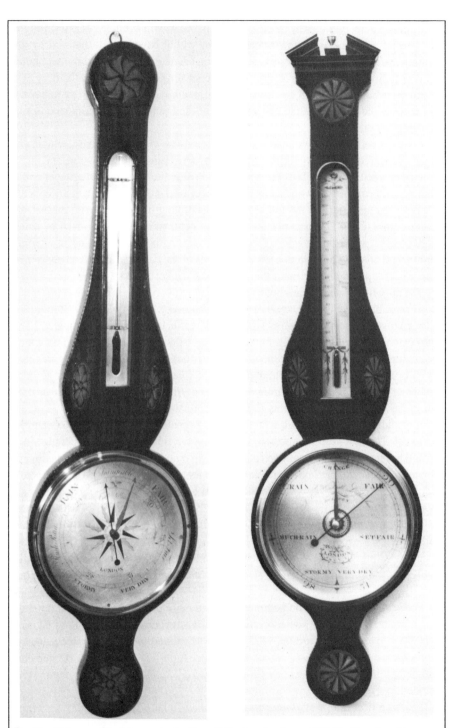

Fig. 12   Mahogany 8 inch barometer by Frans Pellegrino, London, c.1785 (*D. Birt, Canada*).
Fig. 13   Mahogany 8 inch barometer by J. Testi, London, c.1800.

Fig. 14   Mahogany 8 inch barometer by James Vechio, Dublin, c.1810.
Fig. 15   Mahogany 10 inch barometer by Charles Pitsalla, London c.1805.

1750 and known as the 'French taste', although it was popularised in Britain by the Italians. On barometers, this decoration was almost entirely limited to broken pediment mahogany instruments with 8 inch dials and a thermometer as the only additional feature. They were commonly known as Sheraton shell barometers, and were almost invariably veneered in mahogany with ebony and fruitwood stringing, although chequered or zebra stringing was sometimes used as an alternative. Another variation was the use of round shell inlays in place of the two flower head inlays. The inlay patterns were achieved by using different coloured woods with the edges singed to give the impression of shadow. Examples by G. Bianchi, F. Vargo, Mazzuchi & Co. and G. Testi & Co. are given in *Figs* 16–19.

Although the cases were generally veneered with mahogany, more exotic woods, such as rosewood, maple, pearwood and satinwood were sometimes preferred. These woods were considered to be sufficient adornment in themselves and the addition of marquetry was not essential. *Fig.* 20 shows a scroll pediment barometer signed by Corties & Son, 94 Holborn Hill, London, which has a case veneered with satinwood and outlined with stringing and cross-banding which is extended to the thermometer case.

A barometer of around 1820 by A. Barnaschina is a typical 12 inch wheel instrument of the period made by the Italians (*Fig.* 21). A similarly plain, unadorned barometer is shown in *Fig.* 22 by Angelo Alberti of 35 Church Street, Fargate, Sheffield, who was an optician and barometer maker between 1822 and 1828. The shield shape is very rare.

Large numbers of Sheraton shell barometers were mass produced between 1810 and 1825, but they were superseded by the four dial instrument illustrated in *Fig.* 23; around 1840 the four dial instrument acquired a square base (*Fig.* 24). *Fig.* 25 has an unusual pediment but shows the mother-of-pearl inlay against a background of a rosewood veneer that was quite popular from around 1830. The instrument in *Fig.* 26 has the standard scroll pediment and is decorated with trailing foliage of mother-of-pearl. The height is 50.5 inches, including the urn-shaped finial, and its depth is 4 inches. The oat-beard hygrometer and the thermometer are detachable; the thermometer case has a bow glass and this became a feature of cases from around 1830. The clock has an enamel dial but the other four dials are of silvered brass. The rectangular bezel plate is engraved with an urn, swags and foliage and the main dial features the Royal Coat-of-Arms.

An alternative decoration used on the square-cased barometer was the addition of brass columns flanking the mercury thermometer as in *Fig.* 27. The mahogany case is outlined with ebony stringing and is 44 inches in height. The maker was Gillando Broggi, who is recorded as a mathematical instrument maker at Moulsham, Chelmsford. Some barometers have flanking columns of wood.

Fig. 28 shows an attractively shaped and decorated barometer in a rosewood case cross-banded in tulipwood. It was made by Anthony Rivolta, a barometer, thermometer and looking-glass maker of 32 Brooke Street, Holborn, London. He started in business there in 1820 when he took over from his father, Alexander Rivolta.

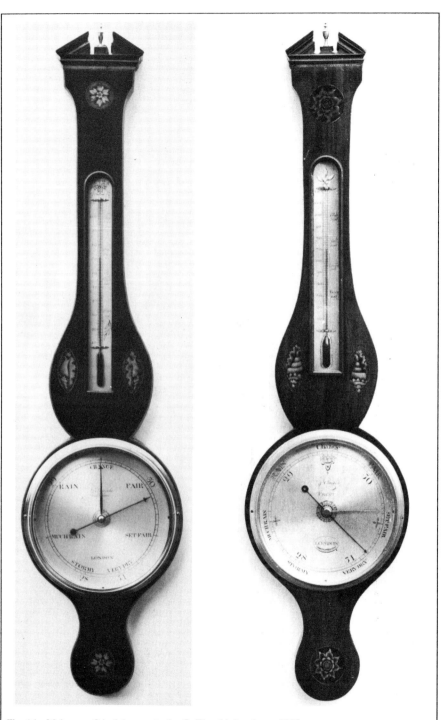

Fig. 16   Mahogany 8 inch barometer by G. Bianchi, London, c.1805.
Fig. 17   Mahogany 8 inch barometer by F. Vargo, London, c.1810 (*Merton Antiques, Merton*).

Fig. 18 Mahogany 8 inch barometer by Mazzuchi & Co., Gloucester, c.1820.
Fig. 19 Mahogany 8 inch barometer by G. Testi & Co., Chester, c.1820.

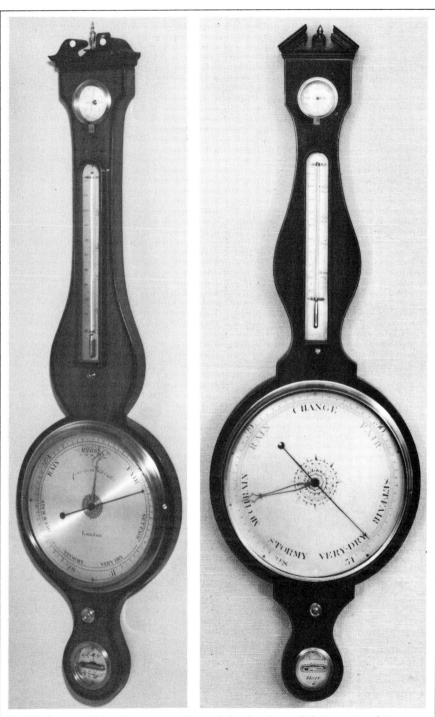

Fig. 20   Satinwood 8 inch barometer by Corties & Son, London, c.1815 (*Asprey, London*).
Fig. 21   Mahogany 12 inch barometer by A. Barnaschina, c.1820 (*Strike One, London*).

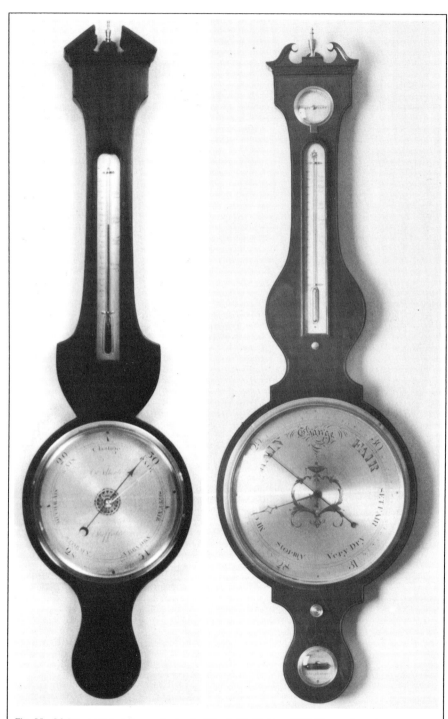

Fig. 22   Mahogany 8 inch barometer by A. Alberti, Sheffield, c.1825 (*P.A. Oxley, Cherhill*).
Fig. 23   Mahogany 10 inch barometer by P. Giusani, Wolverhampton, c.1835 (*D. Birt, Canada*).

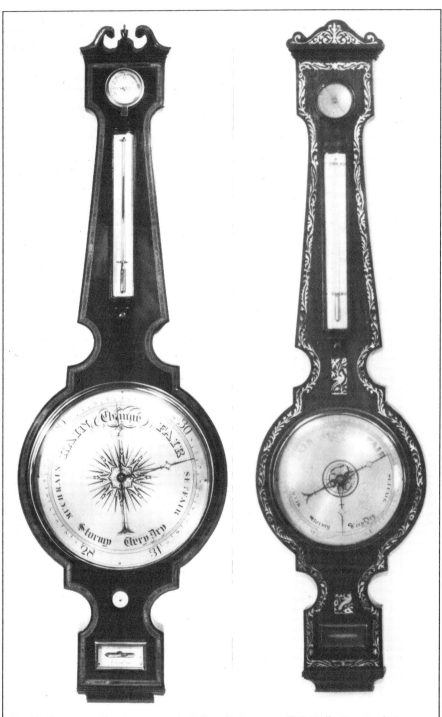

Fig. 24 Mahogany 12 inch barometer by J. Sordelli, London, c.1840 (*Strike One, London*).
Fig. 25 Rosewood 8 inch barometer by M. Barnasconi, Leeds, c.1840 (*Phillips, London*).

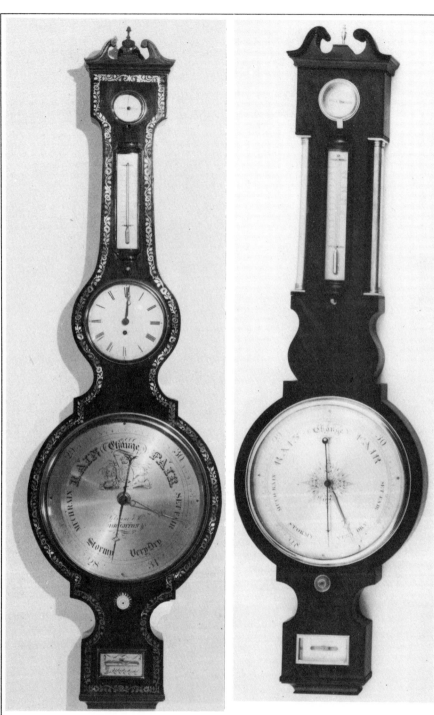

Fig. 26   Rosewood 12 inch barometer by Silvani & Co., Brighton, c.1840 (*Christies, London*).
Fig. 27   Mahogany 10 inch barometer by G. Broggi, Chelmsford, c.1840 (*Sotheby's, London*).

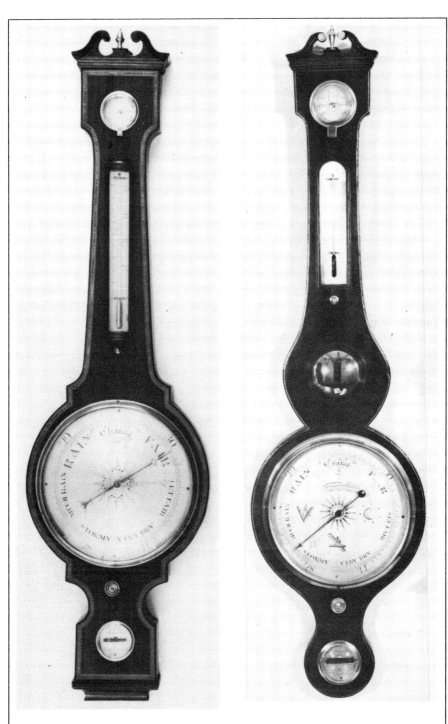

Fig. 28 Rosewood 10 inch barometer by A. Rivolta, London, c.1840 (*Sotheby's, London*).
Fig. 29 Mahogany 8 inch barometer by J. Schalfino, Taunton, c.1845 (*M.W. Cox, Bristol*).

By 1845 the most popular design of wheel barometer was the five dial scroll pediment type shown in *Fig*. 29. It was like earlier instruments except that the thermometer had been shortened so that a convex mirror could be added above the dial. Its purpose appears to have been decorative as all the mirrors were of the convex type and reflected the contents of the hall or room in which the barometer was hung. The level plate is signed 'J. Schalfino, Taunton. Warranted'. He was a prolific maker and most of his instruments are engraved with masonic signs and emblems.

The majority of these barometers had 8 inch dials, but some were made with 10 inch dials as in *Fig*. 30 by P. Introssi of Chatham. This example has a squared section above and below the main dial, while others have a squared section at the base of the instrument (as *Fig*. 28). An unusually shaped barometer is shown in *Fig*. 31 with the thermometer housed neatly on the main dial. The convex mirror has a broad wooden bezel and the finely grained mahogany case has no stringing or other decoration.

The spread of scientific knowledge, coupled with a general increase in wealth among the middle classes, led to a greater demand for barometers from the second decade of the nineteenth century. This resulted in the mass production of barometers which was undertaken by a limited number of makers who sold them wholesale or retail. One result was a deterioration in the quality of the barometers produced and another was a reduction in the variety of case designs available.

During the second half of the nineteenth century the scroll pediment design gave way to the plainer onion-top or tulip-top instrument as shown in *Fig*. 32. The case is veneered with rosewood and is painted with gold paint to resemble brass stringing and brass leaf decoration, which was a feature of some of the more expensive barometers. The onion-top first appeared as a two or four dial barometer and a mirror was added around 1855, but the shape of the onion-top changed progressively during the third quarter of the nineteenth century. At this time there was a return to the two dial barometer with only a main dial and a thermometer.

Expensive wheel barometers made around 1855 are illustrated in *Figs* 33 and 34. The rosewood cases are elegantly inlaid with variegated mother-of-pearl and brass depicting birds, leaves, flowers and urns. The cases of these two barometers and their decoration are almost identical, which suggests that they were made by the same case maker. The barometer shown in *Fig*. 35 made around 1860 by P. Mantova of Luton is profusely and elegantly inlaid with variegated pearl and brass depicting birds, flowers, buds, leaves and the Prince of Wales Feathers above the 8 inch silvered dial. A similar barometer is shown in *Fig*. 36 by F. Pastorelli & Co., London; it is elaborately inlaid in brass and mother-of-pearl with exotic birds, trailing foliage and a cornucopia.

The most popular design of case produced by the Italians in the 1860s is shown in *Fig*. 173 (see chapter 6); these were made of rosewood, walnut, oak or mahogany with round moulded edges.

Carved case barometers became popular in the 1870s. Similar barometers were advertised by L. Casella, Negretti & Zambra and James J. Hicks, an English maker, so that it is clear that several makers obtained their cases from the same cabinet maker. An illustration is given in *Fig*. 37; these barometers reflected the Gothic or medieval

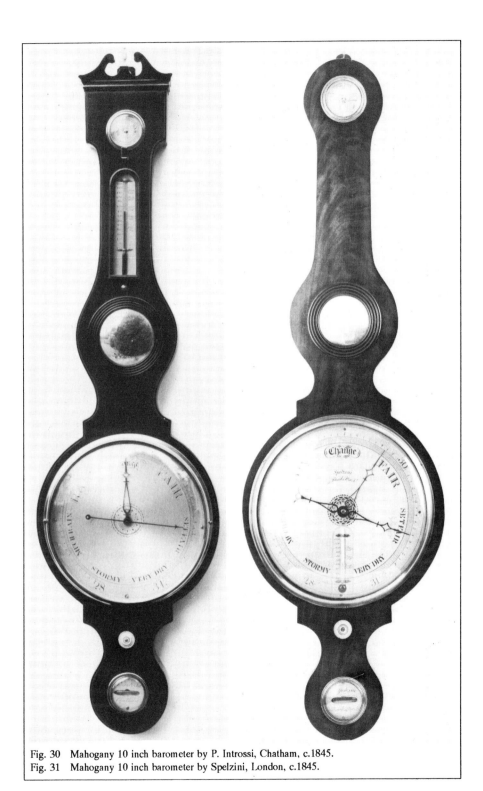

Fig. 30 Mahogany 10 inch barometer by P. Introssi, Chatham, c.1845.
Fig. 31 Mahogany 10 inch barometer by Spelzini, London, c.1845.

Fig. 32   Rosewood 8 inch barometer by P. Bragonzi, Hereford, c.1850.
Fig. 33   Rosewood 10 inch barometer by C. Bregazzi, Hanley, c.1855 (*Sotheby's, London*).

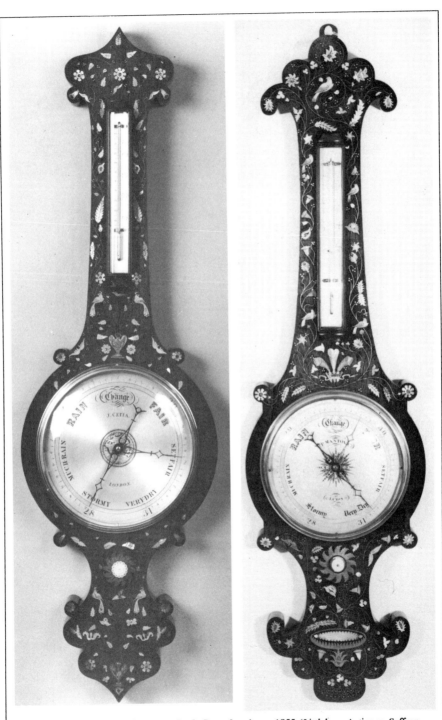

Fig. 34 Rosewood 10 inch barometer by J. Cetta, London, c.1855 (*Littlebury Antiques, Saffron Walden*). Fig. 35 Rosewood 8 inch barometer by P. Mantova, Luton, c.1860 (*M.W. Cox, Bristol*).

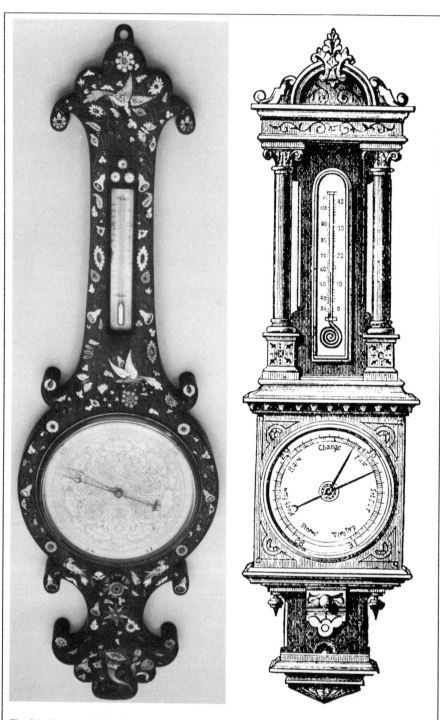

Fig. 36   Rosewood 10 inch barometer by F. Pastorelli & Co., London, c.1860 (*Phillips, London*).
Fig. 37   Carved wheel barometer from the catalogue of L. Casella, London, c.1875.

influence which was revived during the late Victorian period. The cases were variously carved in solid oak, walnut, mahogany or rosewood.

Far fewer mercury wheel barometers were produced during the last quarter of the nineteenth century. The makers could not compete with the much cheaper aneroid instrument, even with mass production methods, and there was no incentive to produce new wheel barometer case designs. Those that were made had cases based on earlier designs and some of the parts used were of inferior quality. In this way the reproduction barometer began.

Domestic Stick or Cistern Tube Barometers

Until the arrival in London of the Italian barometer makers during the last quarter of the eighteenth century, the great majority of stick barometers were fitted with boxwood cistern tubes as shown in *Fig.* 38. The Italians, many of whom were glassblowers, much preferred the glass bulb cistern tube, as shown in *Figs* 39 and 40, and fitted this type of tube to the barometers that they made from around 1780.

The bulb or bottle cistern tube was popular on the Continent from around 1690; the early bulb cisterns were pear-shaped with a small hole in the side to admit air and they later became rounded, still with a hole in the side; later still, the bulb was left open at the top and a further development was that a neck was added.

Its main advantage was that it was easy and cheap to make; this had the effect of reducing the overall cost of the barometer and so made them more widely available. The disadvantages were that it was not so easily made portable as the boxwood type and there was no successful way of determining the scale zero. The only way of adjusting the scale reading was to raise or lower the tube or the register plates; alternatively, the level of mercury in the bulb cistern could be raised or lowered.

The earliest design of bulb cistern barometer made by the Italians can be seen in chapter 4 by Manticha (*Figs* 76 and 77). *Fig.* 41 shows the development of this barometer in a far more elegant mahogany case. The pillared hood is a reminder of earlier clock-case designs, while the decoration and pagoda-type pediment suggests the Chinese Chippendale influence of 1765–70. The bulb cistern is contained within a shallow hinged box, and the tube is held in place by wire threaded through from the back of the case. There are summer and winter weather indications on the printed paper plates which were an Italian innovation. The barometer is signed T.L. Polti, Leeds. This could be the maker who signed his barometers 'Polti from Italy'.

The common type of bulb cistern barometer with paper plates made at the end of the eighteenth century is shown in *Fig.* 42. The moulded case has a mahogany veneer and the pagoda-shaped pediment has three brass finials. The paper plates have standard weather indications and are decorated with two flying cherubs and trailing garlands of leaves. The plates are protected by glass which is fixed flush against them.

This type of barometer had no pretensions to be an accurate instrument; it had no vernier and many had no pointer to record a reading. It was accepted that the bulb cistern tube was not as accurate as the boxwood cistern tube, but they were cheap, attractive and popular and allowed the Italians to gain an entry into the stick barometer

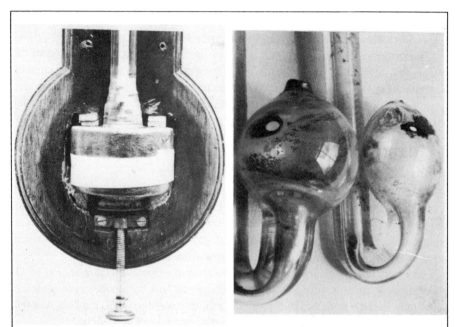

Fig. 38 Fitted boxwood cistern tube.   Fig. 39 Early bulb cistern tubes.

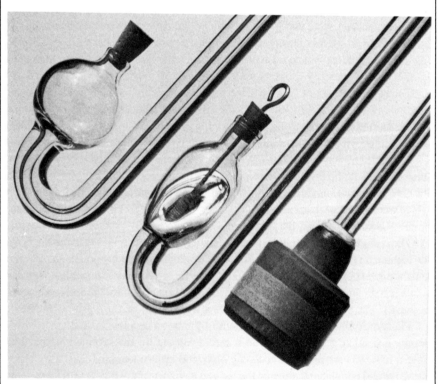

Fig. 40 Two bulb cistern tubes and a boxwood cistern tube.

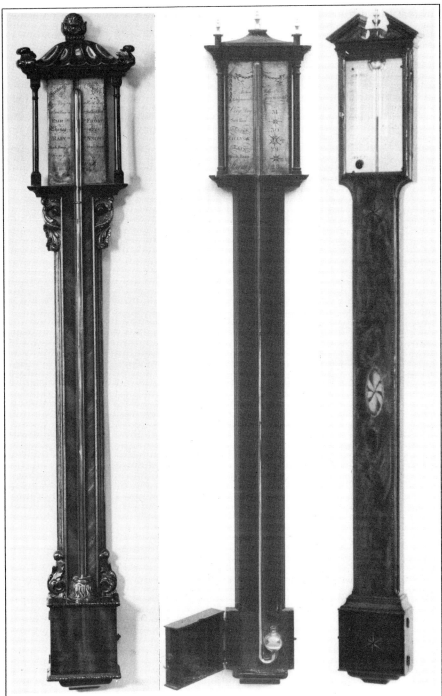

Fig. 41   Mahogany barometer by T.L. Polti, Leeds, c.1790 (*Mallet at Bourdon House Ltd, London*).
Fig. 42   Mahogany barometer by Mathew Woller, Birmingham, c.1800.
Fig. 43   Mahogany barometer by Tarone, Bristol, c.1810 (*J. & M. Bristow, Tetbury*).

market. In fact, these barometers were so much in demand that several English makers copied them; the one illustrated in *Fig.* 42 was made or sold by an Englishman.

The square hinged box type cistern cover was used in conjunction with the broken pediment by the Italians around 1800 as an alternative to the traditional English round turned cistern cover, and an example is given in *Fig.* 43 by Peter A. Tarone. The case is veneered with attractively grained mahogany and is further adorned with typical Italian marquetry in the form of a fan and two six-point star motifs. The silvered brass register plates incorporate an alcohol thermometer and there is a vernier so that accurate barometer readings can be recorded. Protection is provided by a hinged and glazed door. Peter A. Tarone is recorded as a barometer and thermometer maker, working in Tucker Street, Bristol in 1809. He made wheel as well as stick barometers.

The common design of stick barometer popular among Italian makers during the first quarter of the nineteenth century is shown in *Figs* 44–46. The cases were veneered with mahogany, often with a herring-bone pattern, and had moulded edges bordered by stringing or chequered inlay. The shallow turned cistern covers contained bulb cisterns and the silvered brass register plates were protected by glazed doors. A thermometer was added to some register plates and scroll pediments were an alternative to broken pediments. The decoration of the cases was also greatly enhanced by the Italians by the use of stringing and cross-banding with exotic woods and by the use of inlays of leaves, flowers, urns, birds and animals in various woods, brass and mother-of-pearl.

A design of stick barometer made by both Italian and English makers had a bow-fronted case, bowed glass to protect the register plates, a bowed and moulded cornice and urn-shaped cistern cover (see the example by Amadio in chapter 4, *Fig.* 101). The majority of barometers with bow-fronted cases made after 1820 had moulded pediments as illustrated in *Fig.* 47, rather than the scroll pediment. These barometers also had thermometers mounted on the trunk of the case rather than on the register plates. The thermometers were detachable and could be used elsewhere.

An unusual mahogany barometer of the period by N. Tarra, Louth is shown in *Fig.* 48. A hygrometer is mounted above the silvered register plates which have a vernier and thermometer fitted. The shaped cistern cover contains a bulb cistern, and the overall height is 38 inches.

A type of barometer that was invariably made with paper plates and a bulb cistern tube by the Italians is shown in *Fig.* 49. The mahogany case is inlaid with finely drawn geometric floral decoration and the oval cistern cover is inlaid with a large satinwood fan. There are fretwork scrolls to the hood and also a fretwork pediment. There is a simple adjustable pointer behind the glazed door and the plates are signed 'Jno Corti Fecit'. Barometers with similar cases bear English names which suggests that they all obtained their cases from the same maker.

During the early Victorian period, as with wheel barometers, the broken and scroll pediments were, in the main, displaced by square moulded pediments or round tops. Silvered brass was also superseded, over a period, by ivory for register plates and thermometer scales. The bow-fronted design was still popular among Italian makers

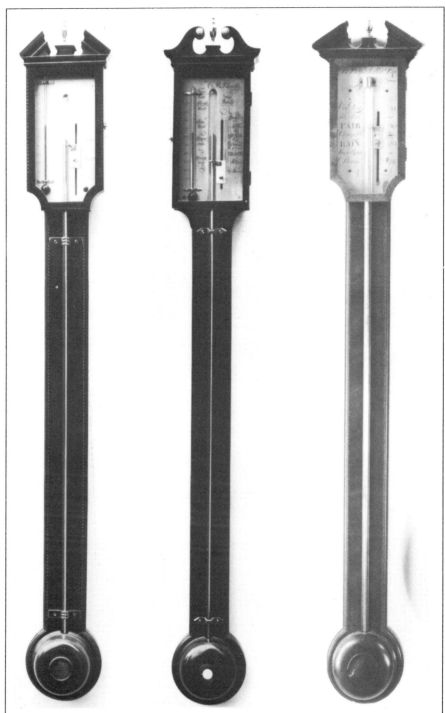

Fig. 44 Mahogany barometer by Peurelly, c.1805. Fig. 45 Mahogany barometer by C.B. Peurelly, c.1810. Fig. 46 Mahogany barometer by J. Bapt. Salla, c.1800.

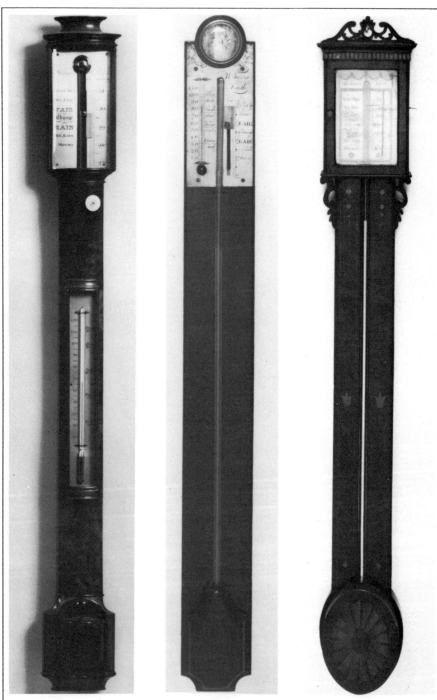

Fig. 47 Mahogany barometer by Dangelo & Cadenazzi, Winchester, c.1820 (*Stair & Co. Ltd, London*). Fig. 48 Mahogany barometer by N. Tarra, Louth, c.1810 (*Sotheby's, London*).
Fig. 49 Mahogany barometer by Jno. Corti, c.1830 (*Sotheby's, London*).

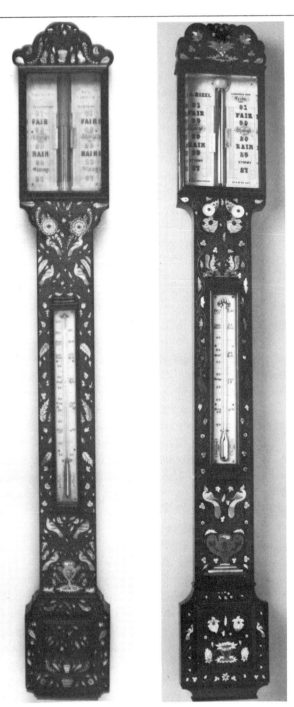

Fig. 50 Rosewood barometer by Primavesi Bros, Poole & Wareham, c.1860 (*Sotheby's, London*).
Fig. 51 Rosewood barometer by A. Rizza, Leeds, c.1860 (*Littlebury Antiques, Saffron Walden*).
Fig. 52 Mahogany marine barometer by C.A. Canti, London, c.1860.

around 1840. The majority of barometers were veneered with rosewood; some were decorated with mother-of-pearl inlay. Two very similar and profusely decorated barometers are shown in *Figs* 50 and 51, dating from around 1860. Both cases are inlaid with leaves, flowers, birds and urns of mother-of-pearl and one has two squirrels. The stems are of brass. Both have square cistern covers and the only material difference is the shape of the pediments. The addresses of the makers on the bone register plates are some 300 miles apart; so it is likely that the cases, at least, were made in London by the same case maker.

During the last quarter of the nineteenth century a very large selection of stick or pediment barometers was available. They were mainly large carved, solid oak instruments with pediments described variously as shield top, shield and point, pointed top, ecclesiastical, round top, castellated top, square top and dome top. The cistern covers were round, square or rectangular and all were heavily carved. These barometers showed the Gothic influence on English furniture design during the last quarter of the nineteenth century. The Victorians aimed to relive the spirit of the Middle Ages by the use of straight lines and solid wood rather than veneer.

The Italians made a limited number of angle barometers from around 1800 and their main contribution to its design was the introduction of the bulb cistern tube. The Italians were also responsible for introducing multiple-tube barometers to Britain, a design which had not been taken up by the English. In 1688 Guillaume Amontons, a Frenchman, had suggested splitting the height of the mercury column by joining together several parallel tubes and filling them alternately with mercury and a lighter liquid, in order to improve the portability of the mercury barometer by reducing its size. Multiple-tube barometers by Manticha and Rabalio are shown in chapter 4 (*Figs* 80 and 81). Multiple-tube barometers were also made by Charles Aiano, James Gatty, Angelo Lovi, Bapt. Ronchetti, Dominico Sala, Charles Silberrad and Torre. Although interesting instruments, they never became popular and were only made for a short period. Their main disadvantages are that the liquids can easily become intermingled when the barometer is carried and the tubes are quickly stained and difficult to clean.

Other Stick or Cistern Tube Barometers

Competition between barometer makers was very keen during the third quarter of the nineteenth century. Factory methods were being used for their production and, in an endeavour to increase sales, some makers began to make barometers for specific purposes, such as the cottage barometer and farmer's barometer. L. Casella and Negretti & Zambra were important makers in this field. Other barometers were made specifically for miners, sailors, travellers and scientists, but only a comparative few of the Italian barometer makers in England entered the scientific instrument market and made marine, station, mountain and scientific barometers and sympiesometers. The most notable of these were L. Casella and Negretti & Zambra in London and Joseph Casartelli in Manchester. All three became large and important businesses and were responsible for developing and patenting various instruments in their particular field.

Quite a number of Italians made marine barometers of the type shown in *Fig.* 52, but these were mainly for use on yachts and small craft and were of a decorative nature. The barometer illustrated, by C.A. Canti, 30 High Holborn, London, is in a cylindrical mahogany case decorated with spiral reeding and gadrooning, while the register plates are of ivory. Marine barometers are always mounted on a gimbals fixed through holes a short distance below the register plates, though the gimbals is missing from the example illustrated.

A sympiesometer is a type of barometer, in which the top part of the tube is filled with hydrogen, while the lower part and the open bulb contain coloured almond oil. While smaller and simpler than the mercury barometer, it has to be handled very carefully and carried almost upright to prevent the air mixing with the liquid. The layout of the sympiesometer can be seen from the pocket-sized instrument illustrated in *Fig.* 53. It is housed in a morocco leather hinged case suitable for travelling or for the pocket. Some were made for calculating altitudes of up to 15,000 feet and these were made in leather sling cases. The base of this instrument is signed 'Peovery, Instrument Maker, London'. The name was probably anglicised to Peover as a William Peover is recorded in the London directories as a mathematical instrument maker in 1855 and again from 1885 to 1897.

Aneroid Barometers and Barographs

The mercury barometer was the prime instrument used for weather forecasting for a hundred and seventy-five years, but its size always made it difficult to carry around. Scientists therefore continued to search for ways of measuring air pressure without the use of mercury, and in 1843 Lucien Vidie, a Frenchman, invented a compact and truly portable aneroid barometer, which began the gradual demise of the relatively expensive but elegant mercury stick and wheel instruments. Eugene Bourdon, another Frenchman, came up with a similar instrument at about the same time but, although popular in France for a while, it was soon found to be less accurate than the Vidie barometer and sales declined rapidly. It was never popular in England and very few were sold.

The early aneroid barometers made under the Vidie patent in commercial quantities had card or silvered metal dials with a diameter of 4.5 inches, and were housed in a brass cylindrical case with a depth of around 2 inches. Barometers with larger dials suitable for hanging in rooms or halls were also made from about 1865, some in carved oak round cases. Some were imported from France and others were made in England by English and Italian makers, but very few were engraved with the maker's or retailer's name. When Vidie's patent expired in 1859, Negretti & Zambra, prompted by Admiral Fitzroy, began to undertake research on the aneroid in an attempt to reduce its size and thus its portability and succeeded in producing pocket and even watch-sized versions (see chapter 6). Negretti & Zambra, Casella, Cetti and Joseph Casartelli were all important makers of aneroid barometers.

Watch-sized barometers were made in silver shut-up cases, very like the hunter watch and, when graduated for heights, were popular with tourists. The one shown in *Fig.* 54 has a 1 inch dial and the scale covers 31 to 21 inches with an outer altitude

Fig. 54 Watch-sized barometer with 1 inch dial in hunter case, c. 1870.

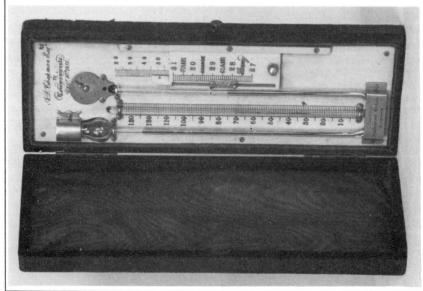

Fig. 53 Pocket sympiesometer by Peovery, London, 1856 (*Walker & Walker, Hungerford*).

Fig. 55   Front view of three pocket barometers with compass, c. 1885.

Fig. 56   Rear view of three pocket barometers with compass, c.1885.

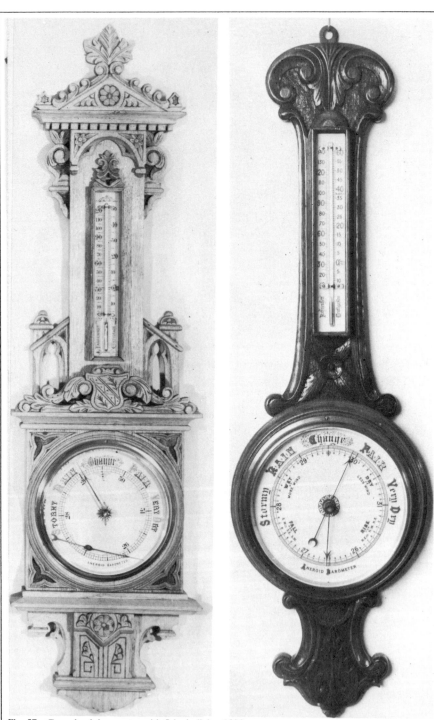

Fig. 57   Carved oak barometer with 8 inch dial, c.1880.
Fig. 58   Carved oak barometer with 8 inch dial, c.1895 (*Harold Judkins, Devizes*).

scale up to 10,000 feet. The owner of this instrument appears to have been a mountaineer as the names and heights of seven mountains are listed, the highest being 7,150 feet.

Travelling sets comprising a barometer, thermometer and compass, and pocket barometers with a compass and sometimes a thermometer, became popular around 1870. They were made by English and Italian makers and some were imported from the Continent. Many of these had no maker's name and some dials were engraved with the name of the owner. Three examples are given in *Figs* 55 and 56. Although one bears a German and another an English name, identical barometers were made by the Italians. Two are in their original velvet double-hinged leather cases and two have delicate curved mercury thermometers. All three have floating head compasses made of mother-of-pearl with jewelled caps. The barometer on the right has a silvered dial of 1.75 inches and was the smallest made, in any quantity, for mountain use.

During the last quarter of the nineteenth century efforts were made by all the makers to popularise the aneroid for use as a household barometer. The result was that a very large number of types and shapes appeared and many of the well-known wheel or banjo-shaped cases were fitted with the then 'modern' aneroid movement. It became difficult to distinguish between mercury and aneroid instruments when viewed from the front; to ascertain whether a barometer was mercury or aneroid, it was necessary to look at the back of the case to see if there was a long door, denoting a mercury instrument, or just a small hole through which to adjust an aneroid movement.

Few of these barometers were signed. *Fig*. 57, in a solid oak case profusely carved in the Gothic manner with flower heads and leaf scrolls, has no name. There is a coat-of-arms in the form of a shield above the porcelain 8 inch dial, and the overall height is 40 inches. A less ornate wall barometer, also unsigned, is shown in *Fig*. 58. The case scroll pattern is carved from solid oak with a height of 34 inches. The porcelain dial is 8 inches in diameter and the first letters of the weather indications are picked out in red. Fitzroy's weather words are painted round the inside of the continuous scale which is protected by bevelled glass in a brass bezel.

Very few mercury barographs were made but aneroid barographs became increasingly popular from around 1875. The Italians, particularly such firms as Negretti & Zambra, contributed in no small way to the development of the aneroid barometer in Britain. Their contribution to scientific research, by producing barometers and other scientific instruments which could more accurately measure air pressure and altitude, greatly assisted mariners, surveyors, aviators and others in the course of their work.

4

Early Italian Makers

One of the best known of the early Italian immigrant barometer makers was James Gatty. Little is known of the history of the Gatty family except that they came from the village of Tavernerio, which is a few miles east of Como in Italy. In the same village lived the Ronchetti and Casartelli families and all three families intermarried. James Gatty appears to have set up in business as a barometer maker in High Holborn, London at least by 1780. He made stick and double barometers, but is best known for his very attractive wheel instruments which were of very high quality. *Figs* 59–62 illustrate four of his barometers with flowing line cases and pleasing decoration. In *Fig.* 59 the pine case is veneered with a deep red mahogany, outlined by triple stringing and with inlays of floral paterae. The Fahrenheit alcohol thermometer has the four heat indications of Blood Heat, Summer Heat, Temperate and Freezing. The silvered dial has horizontal weather indications which formed a feature of many of the early barometers. A feature of the barometer illustrated in *Fig.* 60 is that it has a hinged mahogany bezel with a locking key, as well as a hygrometer and fan-shaped inlays.

Although famed for his wheel barometers, Gatty made very attractive stick instruments and one is shown in *Fig.* 63. The case has wide cross-banding with chequered stringing round the edges and a round turned cistern cover. The register plates and the thermometer are protected by hinged glazed doors and there is an adjustable hygrometer.

An Andrew Gatty is recorded as working in Dublin in 1796 and other Gattys were working in Glasgow, Reading, Manchester and Lewis early in the nineteenth century. A Charles Gatty was working with Charles Malacrida in High Holborn, London between 1803 and 1817 and a 'Domco Gatty' made barometers in High Holborn late in the eighteenth century (*Fig.* 64).

James Gatty also appears to have worked with John Merry Ronketti, as barometers signed Roncheti & Gatty, London are shown in *Figs* 65 and 66. They are very attractive satinwood instruments with hinged wooden bezels and fan-shaped inlays; each has an adjustable hygrometer and set hands which are controlled from above the main dial.

John Merry Ronketti, who also popularised the banjo barometer, came originally, like Gatty, from Tavernerio, Italy. John appears to have been the first member of the family to emigrate to London around 1780. He, too, made a large number of stick and wheel barometers and had the added description of 'artificial flower and feather

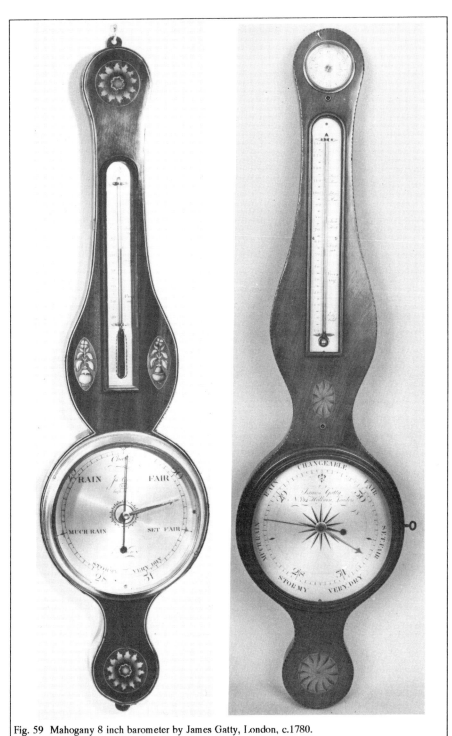

Fig. 59 Mahogany 8 inch barometer by James Gatty, London, c.1780.
Fig. 60 Mahogany 8 inch barometer by James Gatty, London, c.1785 (*Walker & Walker, Hungerford*).

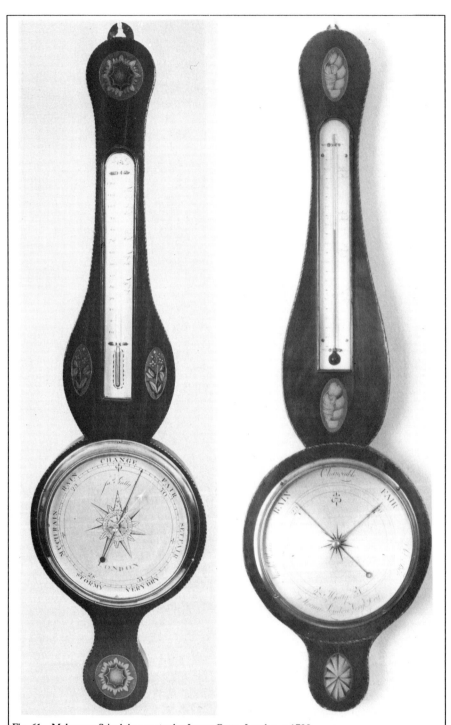

Fig. 61   Mahogany 8 inch barometer by James Gatty, London, c.1790.
Fig. 62   Mahogany 8 inch barometer by James Gatty, London, c.1790 (*D. Birt, Canada*).

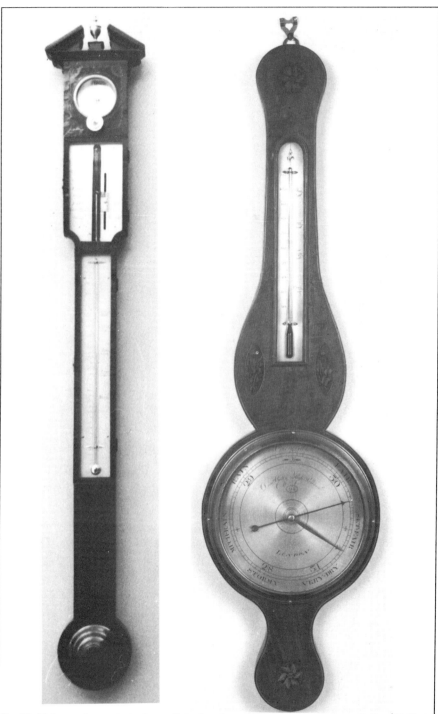

Fig. 63 Mahogany barometer by James Gatty, London, c.1800 (*Littlebury Antiques, Saffron Walden*).
Fig. 64 Mahogany 8 inch barometer by Domco Gatty, London, c.1790 (*Walker & Walker, Hungerford*).

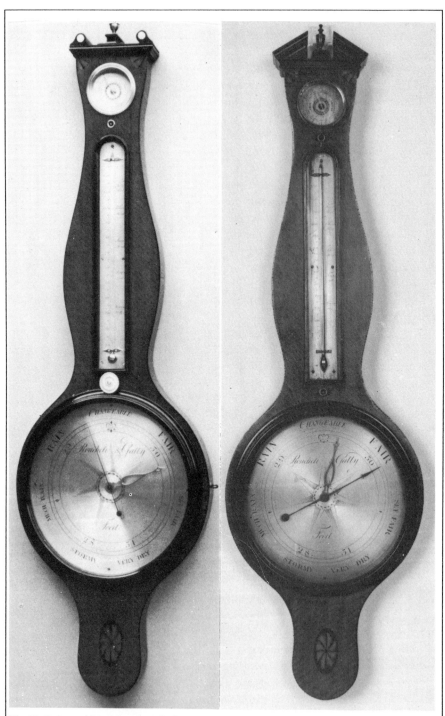

Fig. 65 Satinwood 8 inch barometer by Roncheti & Gatty, c.1790 (*Littlebury Antiques, Saffron Walden*).
Fig. 66 Satinwood 8 inch barometer by Roncheti & Gatty, c.1790 (*Marshall Clare, Stretton*).

manufacturer'. There seems to have been no set spelling of his name, and engravers rendered it variously Ronkite, Roncketi, Ronketi, Roncheti and Ronkitte. He was established at 180 Holborn by 1787 and moved to Bloomsbury around 1800. Three of his wheel barometers are shown in *Figs* 67–69; all three have the address 180 Holborn. The instrument in *Fig.* 69 has a spirit level which is unusual for such an early barometer. Another unusual feature is the pointer for recording thermometer readings, which is adjusted by a rack-and-pinion mechanism operated by the ivory key below the thermometer. Even the Dry/Moist hygrometer is adjustable by a cog mechanism operated by inserting the same key in the hole just below the brass bezel. The key is also used to adjust the brass set hand which is connected by a pulley arrangement behind the dial to the key hole below the dial brass bezel.

A cousin of John Merry Ronketti was (John) Baptist Ronchetti who was the son of Bartolomeo Ronchetti and his wife Francesca née Casartelli. John Baptist was born in 1753 in Tavernerio, Italy and emigrated to Manchester in 1785 and set up in business as a weather-glass maker in 1794 at 15 High Street. Around 1805 he sent to Italy for his son Charles Joshua and his nephew Lewis Casartelli to help him in the business. Baptist, or Baptista as he was also known, was a prolific producer of high-quality instruments which included stick, wheel, angle and double barometers. He returned to Italy in 1807.

A pleasing stick barometer by Baptista Ronchetti is shown in *Fig.* 70. The mahogany veneered case is outlined with chequered stringing and the panelled trunk is adorned with marquetry flower spray patterns similar to those seen on contemporary wheel barometers. The Dry/Moist hygrometer is adjusted by the key below the dial which operates a cog mechanism.

Two of his extemely appealing wheel barometers are illustrated in *Figs* 71 and 72. These are identical except for the marquetry each side of the thermometer and the engraving on all the dials. These barometers could well have been especially commissioned, but they show the exceptionally high standard of workmanship that could be achieved. Baptist Ronchetti appears to have been the only maker of these barometers with lyre-shaped centres and three finials, but where all the parts were made is debatable.

Charles Joshua Ronchetti continued the business until 1809 and then left Manchester and spent a short time with relatives in Holland. He returned to England in 1810 and lived in Shrewsbury, Carlisle and Liverpool before settling in Manchester and working for Vincent Zanetti. In 1817 he set up on his own in Balloon Street as a barometer and thermometer maker and remained in business at various addresses in Manchester until 1841 when he handed over to his two sons, John Baptist and Joshua. Charles Joshua was a friend of Dr John Dalton, the scientist, and John Mercer, the chemist, for whom he produced instruments. He also kept a rain gauge on the wall of his premises and provided weekly weather forecasts for the Manchester press from 1830, which his two sons continued. The business was sold to Lewis Casartelli in 1852.

Other early Italian migrants to Manchester were Vittore Zanetti (*Fig.* 73) and his brother Vincent. They came from Lake Garda, Lombardy around 1795, from a large and prosperous family noted for their fresco paintings and books on pictures, frescoes,

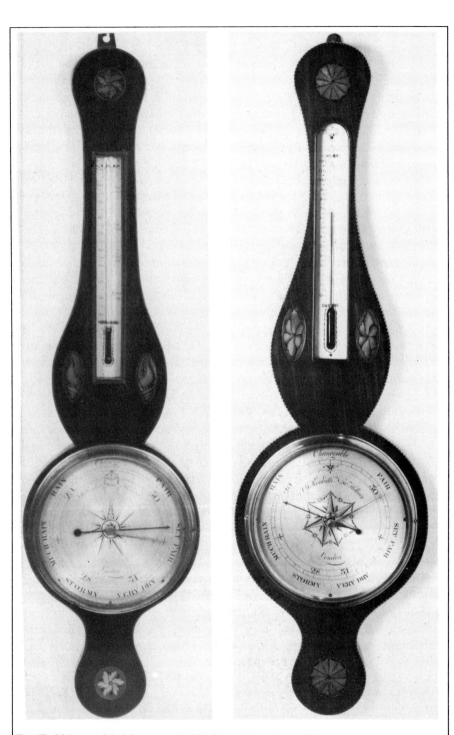

Fig. 67   Mahogany 8 inch barometer by J.M. Ronketti, London, c.1795.
Fig. 68   Mahogany 8 inch barometer by J.M. Ronketti, c.1795 (*Strike One, London*).

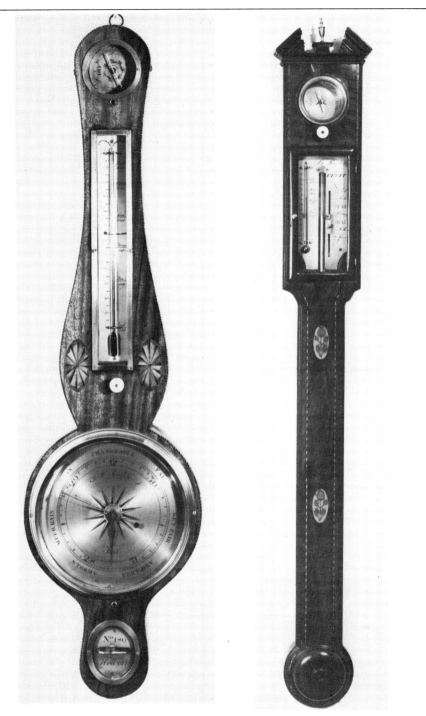

Fig. 69   Mahogany 8 inch barometer by J.M. Roncketti, London, c.1790.
Fig. 70   Mahogany barometer by Bapt. Roncheti, c.1800.

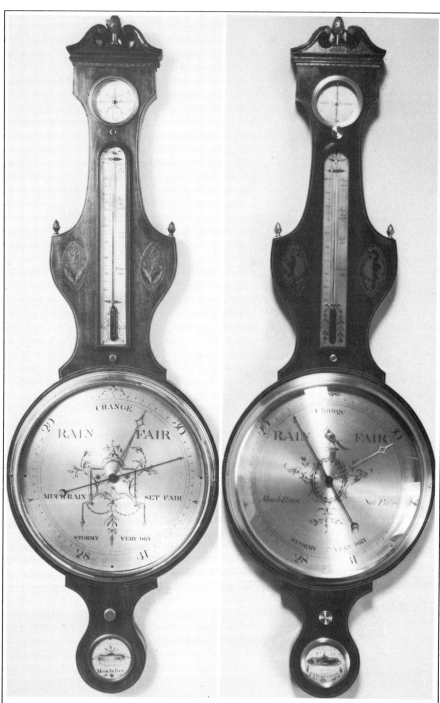

Fig. 71   Mahogany 12 inch barometer by J.B. Roncheti, Manchester, c. 1795 (*Walker & Walker, Hungerford*).   Fig. 72   Mahogany 12 inch barometer by J.B. Roncheti, Manchester, c.1800 (*Littlebury Antiques, Saffron Walden*).

Fig. 73 Vittore Zanetti by H. Wyatt, 1824 (*Thomas Agnew & Sons Ltd, London*).

engravings, statues, inscriptions and seals. Vittore and Vincent were in partnership by 1800 as Zanetti & Co., but they appear to have split up by 1804 as they were working from different addresses in Market Street, although it could have been that Vittore was in charge of the shop and Vincent was responsible for the workshop. In *Pigot and Dean's Directory* of 1819–20, they were described as 'Zanetti Brothers, Repository of Arts'. The same description was given to Zanetti & Agnew, when Vittore took Thomas Agnew into partnership in 1817; they were carvers and gilders, looking-glass and picture frame manufacturers, barometer, thermometer, hygrometer and saccharometer makers, printsellers, publishers, and dealers in ancient and modern gold coins, medals and all kinds of curiosities.

Two examples by Vittore Zanetti of Regency barometers with clocks fitted are shown in *Figs* 74 and 75. The cases are veneered with mahogany and cross-banding and each has a removable clock with an eight-day fusee movement, pendulum and enamel dial.

In 1825 Vittore's son Joseph was made a partner. Vittore retired in 1828 and returned to Lake Maggiore, Italy. The firm was then known as Agnew & Zanetti, Joseph being the junior partner until 1835 when he left to set up in business on his own in Manchester. Agnew then concentrated on the picture and print side of the business and, with his sons William and Thomas, formed a partnership under the name of Thomas Agnew & Sons in 1850. Branches were later opened in Liverpool and London, but the business was eventually consolidated in Old Bond Street, London where it continues to trade today as Thomas Agnew & Sons Ltd.

Another early migrant was Dominick Manticha of 11 Ely Court, Holborn, London. Very little is known of his background, but he was working at 11 Ely Court from at least 1781 to 1805 where he made high-quality stick, wheel and double barometers. His stick barometers had printed paper plates and square-hinged cistern covers. *Figs* 76 and 77 show an example of an early Italian bulb cistern stick barometer by Manticha. The case is of panelled oak with side pillars supporting the moulded flat cornice. Printed paper register plates are used; these are varnished and protected by glass which is placed in position through a slot along the top of the cornice. The weather indications are a mixture of Gothic, Roman and copperplate lettering surrounded by decoration of entwined leaves, grapes and flowers. At the top of the plates are two winged cherubs with a cockatoo and a peacock at the bottom. Access to the cistern is by unscrewing the base of the cistern cover and the twisted wire pointer is operated manually up and down a brass rod behind the right-hand pillar.

Two of Manticha's high-quality wheel barometers are shown in *Figs* 78 and 79. *Fig.* 78 is a mahogany instrument decorated with marquetry in the form of fan and six-point star motifs; the fans are of satinwood with sand-burnt shading lines and the edging lunettes are of harewood, a contrasting wood. The wooden bezel extends almost to the edge of the case, and the veneers on the sides of the case are laid across, rather than along, the length of the case, a sure sign of quality. *Fig.* 79 is an attractively cased barometer by Manticha with a lockable wooden bezel and unusual shell inlay.

Manticha also made double or multiple-tube barometers, and one of his is illustrated

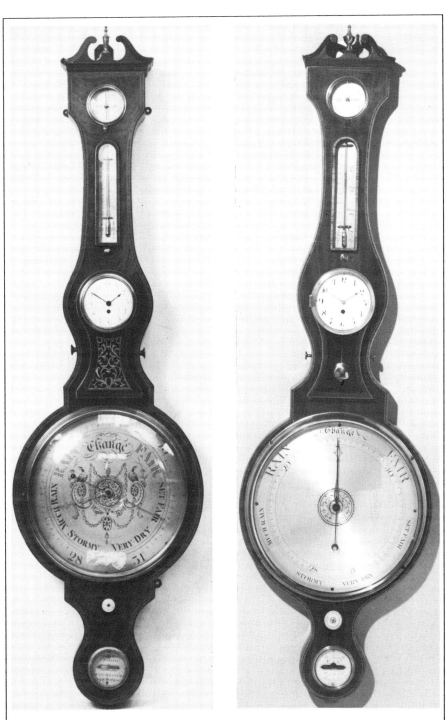

Fig. 74   Mahogany 12 inch barometer by V. Zanetti, Manchester, c.1815 (*Patric Capon, London*).
Fig. 75   Mahogany 12 inch barometer by V. Zanetti, Manchester, c.1815 (Asprey, London).

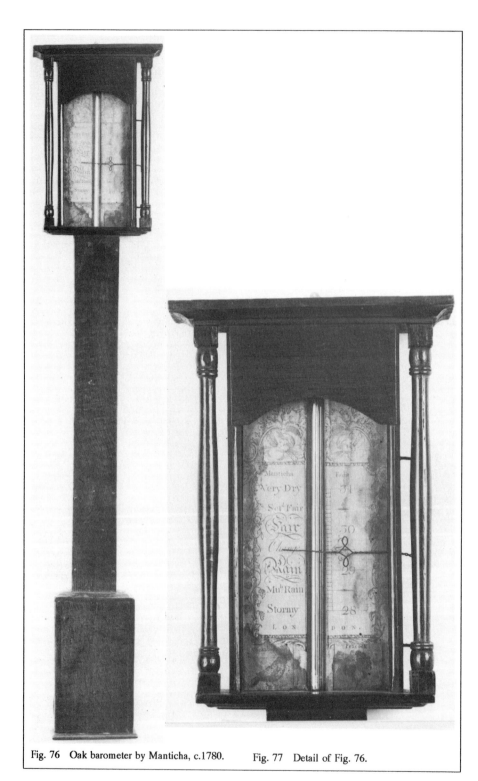

Fig. 76 Oak barometer by Manticha, c.1780.   Fig. 77 Detail of Fig. 76.

70

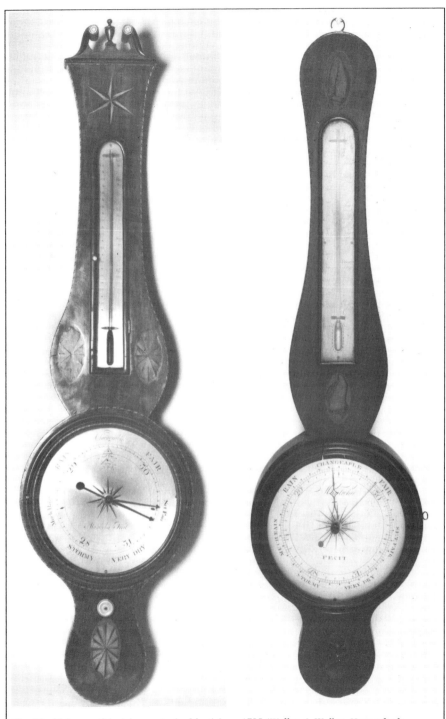

Fig. 78 Mahogany 8 inch barometer by Manticha, c.1785 (*Walker & Walker, Hungerford*).
Fig. 79 Mahogany 8 inch barometer by Manticha, c.1790 (*Sotheby's, London*).

in *Fig*. 80, made in 1781. The mahogany case has a glazed door which is arched and has three finials of brass. The printed paper register plates are glued onto boxwood and are decorated with pillars festooned with leaves, flowers and fruit and capped with masonic signs, birds and human figures. A spirit thermometer is on the left and the four connected tubes on the right are headed 'Double Barometer'. Mercury and oil are used alternately in the tubes and the level of the oil in the open right-hand side tube indicates the atmospheric pressure; the lower the pressure the higher the oil rises in the tube. The barometer is 24 inches high, and by using the oil in conjunction with mercury the scale is extended to 15 inches, compared with 3 inches for the normal stick barometer. A similar barometer made about 15 years later by Rabalio is shown in *Fig*. 81. The main difference is that the thermometer scales and weather indications are stamped on a boxwood base. It also has a set hand that slides up and down a brass wire which is secured at the top and bottom of the door frame.

Some extant wheel, stick and double barometers of the same period bear the signature of Peter Manticha, Crown Feather Court, Holborn; also Manticha & Co., London. These are likely to be family connections. A wheel barometer signed Manticha & Co., London is illustrated in *Fig*. 82.

The barometer illustrated in *Fig*. 83 is by P. Gally, London. It has a scroll pediment with unusual inlay decoration and high-quality engraving on the dial consisting of leaf and flower scrolls. P. Gally is not recorded in the London directories in the eighteenth century, but Peter and Paul Gally are recorded as having started in business in Clerkenwell, London in 1809 as barometer, looking-glass and picture frame makers and were working there, and later in Hatton Garden until 1861. They were probably the sons of P. Gally and were followed in Hatton Garden by Charles Gally who traded there alone until 1882.

Another important early maker was Joseph Somalvico of 67 Leather Lane, London. An example of one of his many fine wheel barometers is given in *Fig*. 84. The veneered case is adorned with chequered stringing and flower head and flower spray marquetry. This barometer, and others, suggests that Joseph Somalvico must have arrived in London by 1780, and with his two sons, James and Charles, made a large number of pleasing barometers.

He also made barometers in partnership with Dominick Lione. An interesting example is shown in *Fig*. 85 with the thermometer mounted on the barometer dial. The case is veneered with attractively grained mahogany, and it could be that they wished to leave as much mahogany exposed as possible. *Fig*. 86 shows another barometer by the partnership with the thermometer on the main dial, but it also has a clock and a hygrometer. Both partners were recorded at 125 Holborn Hill in 1805 and then Brooke Street in 1811 until 1822. Somalvico's two sons, James and Charles, became barometer makers; as did the two sons of James Lione, named Joseph and Vincent. Vincent ceased business in 1858, but Joseph flourished and continued making barometers into the twentieth century. Lione & Somalvico were notable makers who did not always conform to the popular shell and flower head inlay motif. They sometimes preferred an inlay depicting an urn containing leaves and flowers as shown in *Fig*. 87.

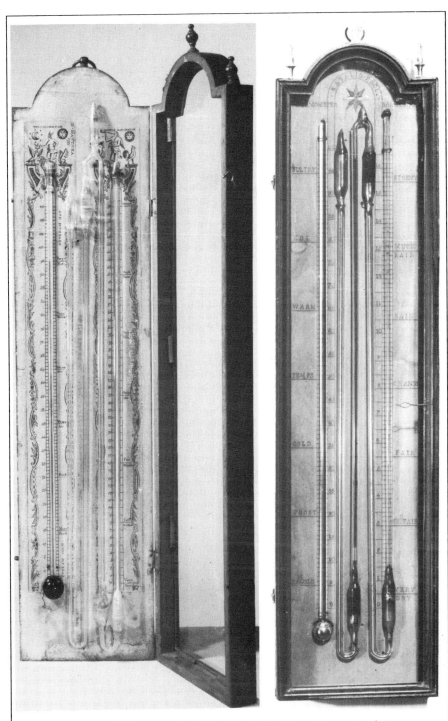

Fig. 80   Mahogany double barometer by D. Manticha, 1781 (*Science Museum, London*).
Fig. 81   Mahogany double barometer by Rabalio, c.1795 (*Marshall Clare, Stretton*).

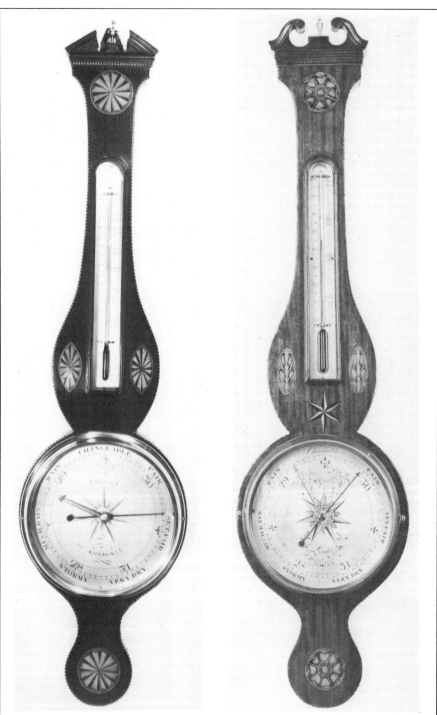

Fig. 82   Mahogany 8 inch barometer by Manticha & Co., London, c.1810 (*Strike One, London*).
Fig. 83   Mahogany 8 inch barometer by P. Gally, London, c.1790.

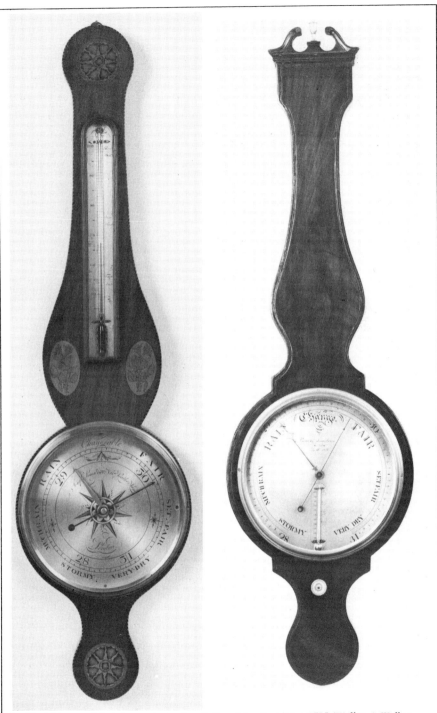

Fig. 84   Mahogany 8 inch barometer by Joseph Somalvico, London, c.1785 (*Walker & Walker, Hungerford*).   Fig. 85   Mahogany 10 inch barometer by Lione & Somalvico, London, c.1805.

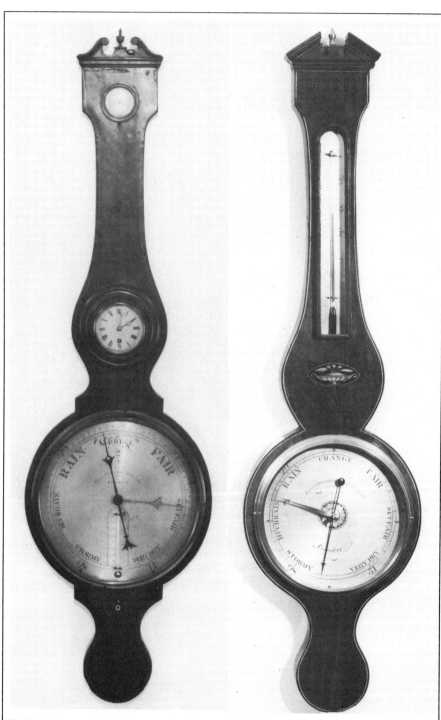

Fig. 86   Mahogany 12 inch barometer by Lione & Somalvico, London, c.1805 (*Phillips, London*).
Fig. 87   Mahogany 8 inch barometer by Lione & Somalvico, London, c.1815.

'Somalvico & Son' were trading from 37 Charles Street, Hatton Garden around 1835 when the barometer in *Fig.* 88 was made. It has weather indications in French added below those in English, which suggests that it was taken to and used in France. At the bottom of the dial it is engraved with the name and address of the French firm who repaired it; it is likely to have been engraved with the French weather indications when it was repaired. *Fig.* 89 shows an onion-top barometer by Joseph Somalvico & Co., 2 Hatton Garden, London made around 1855. Scrolls of rosewood decorate the onion shapes at the top and bottom of the case which is veneered with bird's eye maple.

An example of a stick barometer, with the addition of a hygrometer, by Joseph Somalvico when he was at 67 Leather Lane, Holborn, can be seen in *Fig.* 90. The panel housing the adjustable hygrometer is decorated with fan-shaped marquetry and a boxwood cistern tube is used, the evidence being the adjustable screw at the base of the case used to make it portable. The Italians seem to have preferred using boxwood cisterns when making the best quality barometers. Stick barometers were also produced by Somalvico in conjunction with Lione. The barometer shown in *Fig.* 91 signed by Lione, Somalvico & Co., 125 Holborn Hill can be accurately dated to around 1805 as the firm was only trading from this address from 1805 to 1807. This style was produced in large quantities and was still being made into the 1830s.

Fig. 92 shows a bow-fronted stick barometer by J. Somalvico, London; a design which remained popular into the middle of the nineteenth century. The majority of this design were veneered with rosewood, and not many were decorated with mother-of-pearl inlay and trailing leaves and flowers as this barometer. Another attractive instrument, this time signed 'Josh. Somalvico & Co., London', and also inlaid with mother-of-pearl is shown in *Fig.* 93. It has a bow-fronted case and moulded pediment. The cistern cover is ebonised and the trunk is decorated with leaves, flowers and birds of mother-of-pearl. The ivory register plates have two recording verniers; one for '10 A.M. Yesterday' and the other for '10 A.M. Today'.

A barometer signed Lione & Co., 81 Holborn, London is shown in *Fig.* 94. The mahogany case is outlined in boxwood and ebony stringing and inlaid with further cross-banded borders to the timepiece and hygrometer. The clock has a fusee and chain movement with verge escapement and a 4.5 inch enamel dial.

James Lione was the maker of the barometers in *Figs* 95 and 96, which demonstrate what an important and innovative maker he was. The mahogany barometer in *Fig.* 95 has cross-banding and a 12 inch dial with an eight-day clock which has an enamel dial. The 'upside-down' mahogany barometer in *Fig.* 96 has a 10 inch dial and a height of 37 inches. Although the case is a pleasing design, it never became popular, possibly because the dial has to be so far above the short limb of the tube; this makes it necessary for the pulley threads to be over 24 inches long, at which length they become easily tangled and caught up in the case.

F. Amadio & Son were prolific makers of high-quality barometers from early in the nineteenth century until 1865. Little is known of the Amadio family; Francis appears to have set up in business around 1800 at 118 St John St Road, London and was in

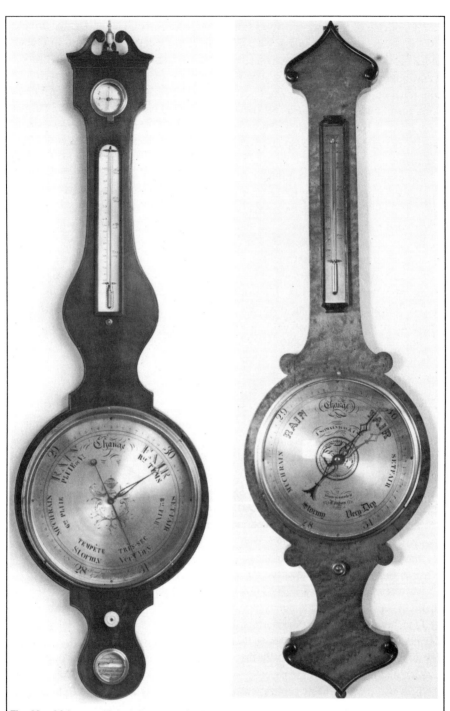

Fig. 88   Mahogany 12 inch barometer by Somalvico & Son, London, c.1835 (*Walker & Walker, Hungerford*).   Fig. 89   Bird's eye maple 10 inch barometer by J. Somalvico & Co., London, c.1855 (*Walker & Walker, Hungerford*).

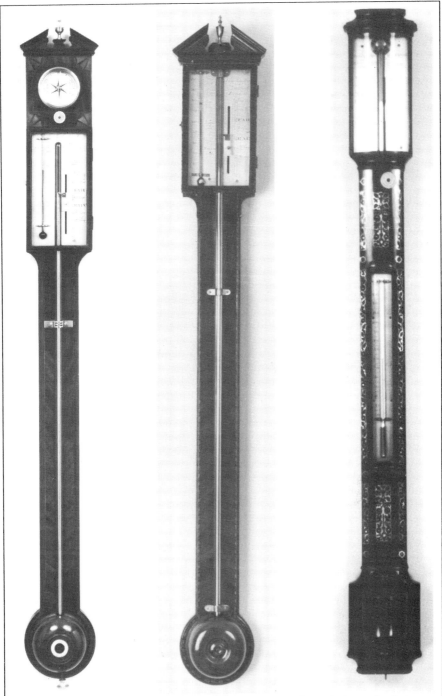

Fig. 90   Mahogany barometer by Joseph Somalvico, London, c.1805 (*Patric Capon, London*).
Fig. 91   Mahogany barometer by Lione Somalvico & Co., London, c.1805 (*D. Birt, Canada*).
Fig. 92   Rosewood barometer by J. Somalvico, London, c.1840 (*P.A. Oxley, Cherhill*).

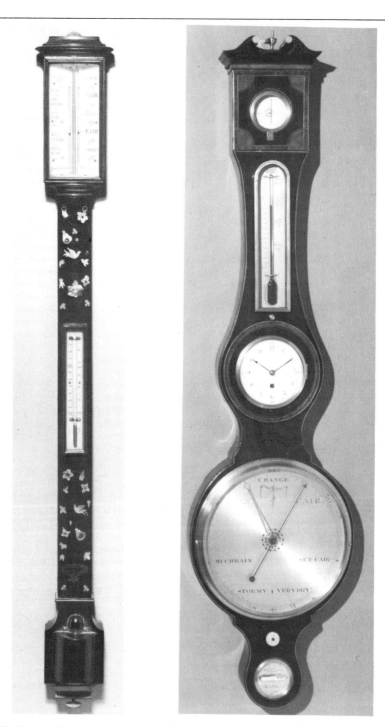

Fig. 93   Rosewood barometer by Josh. Somalvico & Co., London, c.1850 (*Sotheby's, London*).

Fig. 94   Mahogany 10 inch barometer by Lione & Co., London, c.1810 (*Asprey, London*).

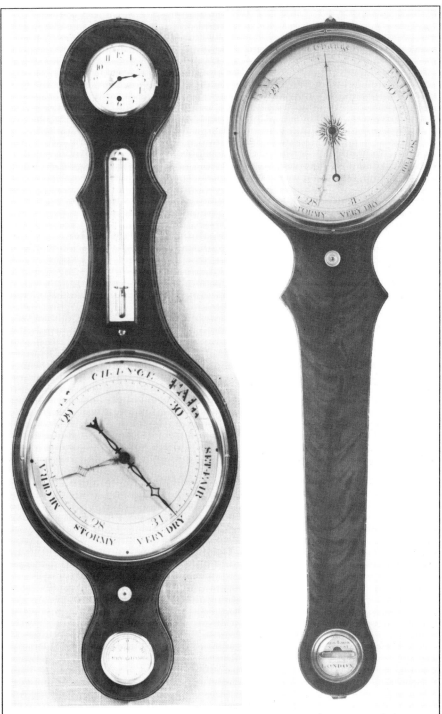

Fig. 95 Mahogany 12 inch barometer by J. Lione, London, c.1820 (*Patric Capon, London*).
Fig. 96 Mahogany 10 inch barometer by James Lione, London, c.1820.

partnership with a son, also Francis. The partnership seems to have been formed soon after the father started in business as some barometers signed F. Amadio & Son appear to have been made very early in the nineteenth century.

An early unusual round-top barometer by F. Amadio & Son is shown in *Fig.* 97. It is veneered in mahogany with zebra stringing and has uncustomary paterae decoration. The alcohol Fahrenheit thermometer has two additional heat indications of Fever Heat at 112 degrees and Extreme Cold at Zero. *Fig.* 98 shows an Amadio scroll or swan-necked barometer with an 8 inch dial. The pine case is veneered with mahogany and outlined with ebonised and fruitwood stringing. There is a brass finial on a platform between the scrolls of the pediment, and the hygrometer and thermometer are detachable for use elsewhere.

Two contrasting Amadio barometers are reproduced in *Figs* 99 and 100. *Fig.* 99 has a 4.5 inch dial, which was the smallest wheel instrument made in commercial quantities and is now classed as rare. The dial is engraved 'F. Amadio & Son, 118 St John St Road, London', while the level plate is engraved 'J. Mangiacavalli, 22 Charles Street, Hatton Garden'. Amadio was no doubt the maker, and Mangiacavalli the retailer, but it is unusual for both the maker's and retailer's names to be engraved on a barometer as the retailer would normally wish to give the impression that he was the maker. The well-inlaid barometer in *Fig.* 100 is signed 'J. Amadio, 6 Shorters Court, Throgmorton Street, City'. He was probably the son of Francis Amadio junior, as this barometer dates from about 1855. The rosewood case has moulded edges and is profusely inlaid with cut mother-of-pearl foliate decoration and mounted with a bow-fronted thermometer with Fahrenheit and Reaumur scales. It has a scroll top and a height of 44.75 inches; the dial is engraved with a projection of Europe, Africa, Asia and Australia.

That F. Amadio & Son also made stick barometers is demonstrated by the fine example in *Fig.* 101. It is veneered with attractively grained mahogany on a pinewood base which is bow-fronted; it also has bowed glass to protect the register plates and a bowed and moulded cornice. An ebonised urn-shaped cistern cover is used for the boxwood cistern tube and there is ebony inlay on each side of the cistern cover.

The name of Tagliabue was well known in the barometer trade in London during the first half of the nineteenth century. Cesare Tagliabue was born in 1767 near Como, Italy but it is not known when he emigrated to England. He is first recorded as working at 294 High Holborn, London in 1799 and around 1820 moved to Hatton Garden where he took Louis Pascal Casella into partnership trading as Tagliabue & Casella. Casella had, in 1837, married Marie Louise, Tagliabue's eldest daughter, who worked in the office. Cesare was a very successful barometer and scientific instrument maker and from 1813 he started to export instruments to Rio de Janeiro, Spain and Italy. He died in 1844, after which Casella carried on the business which still flourishes today under the name of Casella London Ltd (see chapter 5).

A very elegant satinwood barometer made by Tagliabue & Torre at 294 Holborn, London is shown in *Fig.* 102. The case has an overall height of 45 inches and it has outline stringing and is cross-banded in kingwood. The pediment has an ivory finial with two matching ivory rosettes at the top of each scroll. Convex glasses are fitted

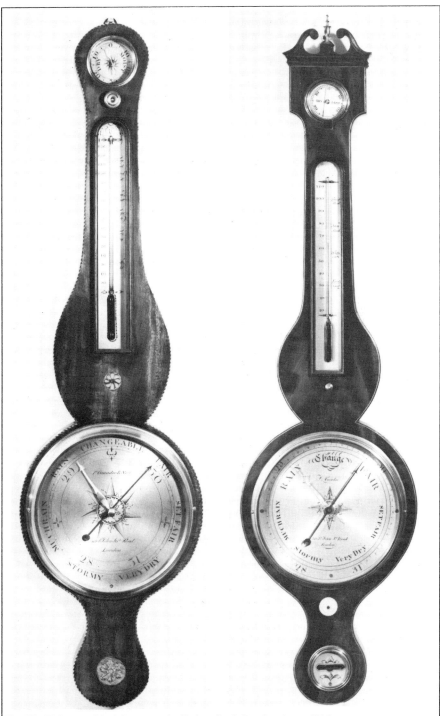

Fig. 97   Mahogany 8 inch barometer by F. Amadio & Son, London, c.1805.
Fig. 98   Mahogany 8 inch barometer by F. Amadio, London, c.1830.

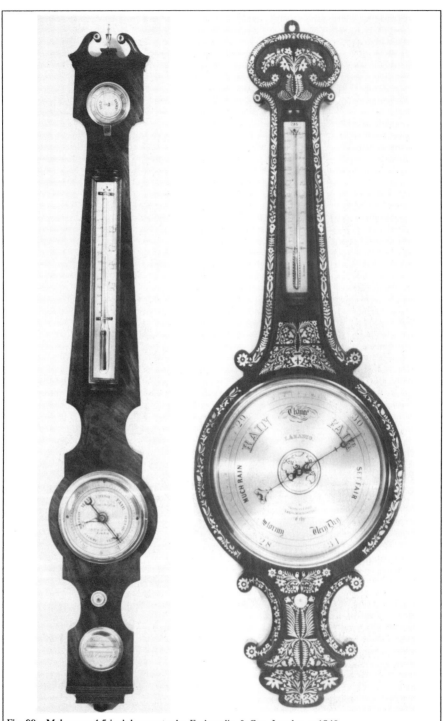

Fig. 99 Mahogany 4.5 inch barometer by F. Amadio & Son, London, c.1840.
Fig. 100 Rosewood 11.5 inch barometer by J. Amadio, London, c.1855 (*Phillips, London*).

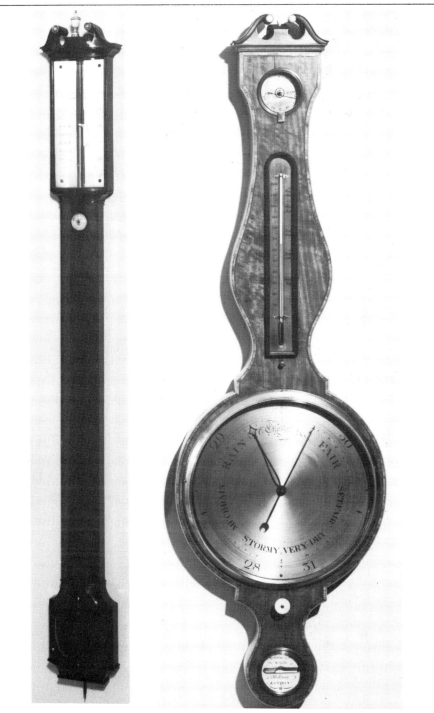

Fig. 101   Mahogany barometer by F. Amadio & Son, London, c.1805 (*Asprey, London*).
Fig. 102   Satinwood 12 inch barometer by Tagliabue & Torre, London, c.1805.

to all three brass bezels, but the thermometer case has a flat glass. An unusual barometer by Cesare Tagliabue is illustrated in *Fig*. 103 with flower head inlays at each end of the case. The hygrometer is set in the middle of the case and the thermometer plate and dial engraving is particularly elaborate. The partnership with Torre seems to have ended about 1807, and this barometer was made when he was on his own, working at 26 Holborn between 1807 and 1814.

Cesare was working at 23 Hatton Garden, London between 1829 and 1838 when he made the mahogany stick barometer shown in *Fig*. 104. This was by far the most popular design of stick barometer produced during the second quarter of the nineteenth century. The pine frame is veneered to give a herring-bone pattern and the shallow turned cistern cover contains a bulb cistern tube.

John, Anthony and Angelo Tagliabue, probably the sons of Cesare, were all barometer makers in Holborn during the second quarter of the nineteenth century, and four firms with the name of Tagliabue were operating there between 1820 and 1845. The three named all used 11 Brooke Street at some time to conduct their business and a Charles Tagliabue was also there in 1835. Angelo Tagliabue is the maker of the 12 inch dial barometer shown in *Fig*. 105 with a rectangular level plate. It has a height of 48 inches and a depth of 4 inches; the address is given as 11 Brooke Street.

Lewis Gianna of Shrewsbury, who made barometers of a very high quality early in the nineteenth century, seems to have had a connection, possibly by marriage, with a Tagliabue in Holborn, probably Cesare Tagliabue as they both made very similar barometers. The connection is strengthened by the fact that a barometer bearing a level plate signed 'L. Gianna, Salop' was found to be signed 'Tagliabue, High Holborn, London' on the reverse side. This suggests that Gianna purchased his barometers or their parts from Tagliabue.

An advertisement by Gianna in the *Salopian Journal* dated 29 March 1809 reads:

> Warranted Barometers. A Farmer of Grazier without a Weather Glass is just like a Mariner without a Compass. Lewis Gianna, Barometer and Thermometer Maker, at the Trumpet Inn, Mardol. Begs leave to inform the Public that he still remains in Shrewsbury and will be happy to supply them with good Barometers and improved Thermometers as any in the Kingdom, and at as reasonable Prices. He needs only mention that the false economy of saving a trifle of Money for an Article of such Value and Utility, subjects many to Losses and Injuries they would afterwards be glad to have avoided.
> Perpendicular Barometers from 10s 6d to £2 2s 0d.
> Wheel Barometers from £2 2s 0d to £12 12s 0d.
> And all other Barometers he makes and warrants.
> Barometers delivered without any further expense within 30 miles of Shrewsbury. Old Barometers and Thermometers repaired on the lowest terms.
> Letters post-paid will be attended to.
> N.B. Lewis Gianna assures his Friends that no person is authorised by him to travel in his name.

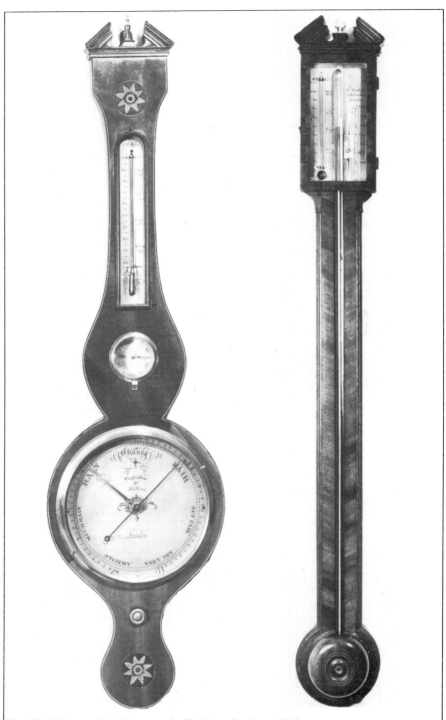

Fig. 103 Mahogany 8 inch barometer by Tagliabue, London, c.1810.
Fig. 104 Mahogany barometer by C. Tagliabue, London, c.1830.

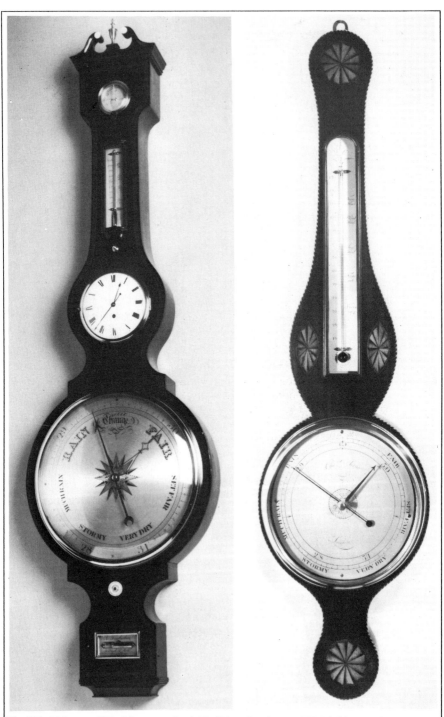

Fig. 105   Mahogany 12 inch barometer by A. Tagliabue, London. c. 1835 (*Littlebury Antiques, Saffron Walden*).   Fig. 106   Mahogany 8 inch barometer by Chas Aiano, London, c.1805 (*Strike One, London*).

A price range of two to twelve guineas suggests that Gianna offered a very wide range of wheel barometers and it is surprising to see that the stick or perpendicular barometer range was limited from half a guinea to two guineas. Gianna died in 1816, 'in consequence of having slept in a damp bed' the *Salopian Journal* records.

Charles Aiano was a clock, barometer and thermometer maker and optician who was born in Canterbury in 1784. He was the son of Christmas Aiano, who was born in Como, Italy, and his wife Mary, née Polletti, who were married in 1782 at St Giles in the Fields, Middlesex. Charles Aiano worked from 1826 to 1841 in Northgate, Canterbury. From 1845 to 1848 he worked in Artillery Street and in 1851 he is recorded at 16 Union Street.

He did not obtain his Freedom of the City of Canterbury, and as it appears that he did not start in business in that city until he was 42, it is reasonable to suppose that he was the same Charles Aiano who was working in London for around 20 years before returning to Canterbury. There is no record of his father's occupation and he could well have gone to London to serve an apprenticeship. Similar high-quality wheel, stick and double barometers signed Aiano, London and Aiano, Canterbury are extant which also suggests that he worked in London and Canterbury. He died in 1859. Two wheel barometers by him are shown in *Figs* 106 and 108. The second barometer illustrated is of an unusual shape and is veneered with satinwood and has cross-banded edges and fan inlay corners on the square hygrometer section. An interesting double-tube barometer by Charles Aiano is shown in *Fig*. 107, which has two bulb cistern tubes; the lower tube covers the scale from 28 to 29.5 inches and the upper tube covers 29.5 to 30 inches. There is a ring recording device fitted to each tube and these are adjusted by wormed rods, the ends of which can be seen at the extreme right-hand side of the barometer arm. The case is veneered with a deep red mahogany and is decorated with chequered stringing and four six-point stars. Aiano also made stick barometers.

Francis Anone was an important Italian maker who arrived in London very early in the nineteenth century. He made and sold high-quality barometers, thermometers, telescopes and prints. Two of his barometers are illustrated in *Figs* 109 and 110. The first is very attractively shaped and veneered in satinwood with outline cross-banding, while the hygrometer is set in an unusual position to maintain balance and symmetry. The example in Fig. 110 is also veneered with satinwood and cross-banded, but it has an unusual pagoda-style pediment.

A fine early Sheraton shell barometer is illustrated in *Fig*. 111 made by P.L.D. Martinelli & Co., Manufactory, 82 Leather Lane, London who was first recorded at this address in 1799. The firm, probably three brothers, could have been at this address earlier because by 1802 D. Martinelli was working at 34 Gray's Inn Road and a Ronketti was in partnership with him there in 1805. Lewis Martinelli remained at 82 Leather Lane and was later in partnership with his son until 1840. Other members of the Martinelli family were Alfred who was working in Lambeth from 1839 until his death in 1851 and William who was working at various London addresses between 1839 and 1880.

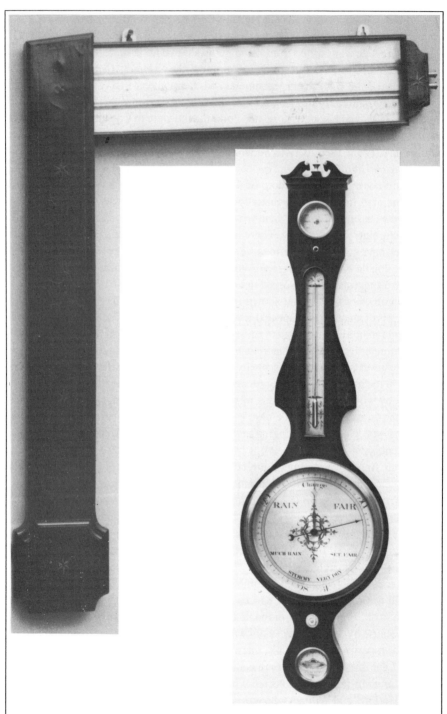

Fig. 107 Mahogany angle barometer by Charles Aiano, c.1800 (*Littlebury Antiques, Saffron Walden*).
Fig. 108 Satinwood 10 inch barometer by C. Aiano, c.1805.

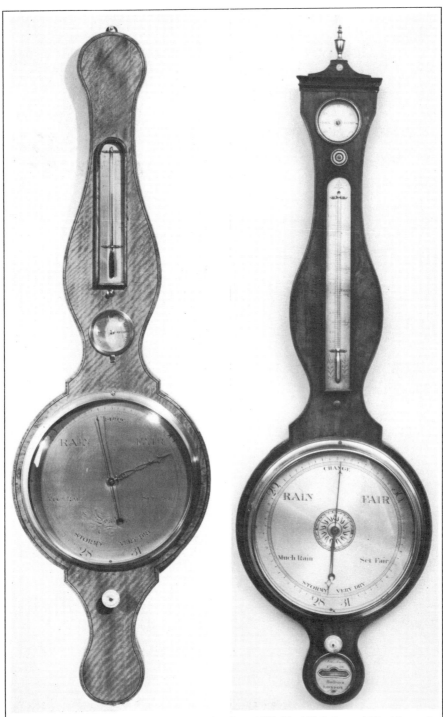

Fig. 109 Satinwood 10 inch barometer by Anone, London, c.1805. Fig. 110 Satinwood 10 inch barometer by Fran Anone, London, c.1805 (*Anthony Preston Antiques Ltd, Stow-on-the-Wold*).

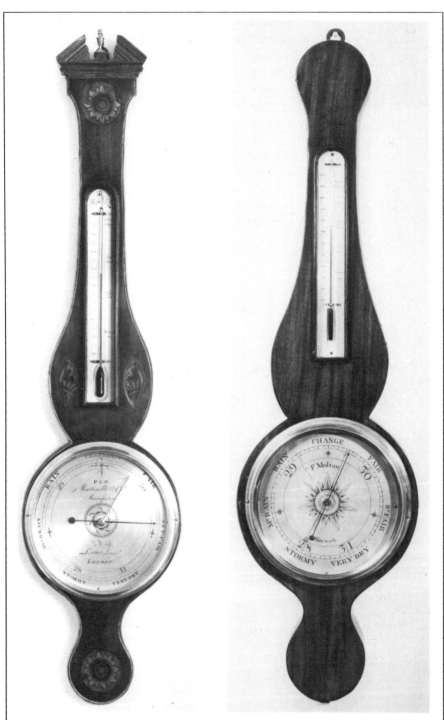

Fig. 111 Satinwood 8 inch barometer by P.L.D. Martinelli & Co., London, c.1800 (*Walker & Walker, Hungerford*). Fig. 112 Mahogany 8 inch barometer by F. Molton, Norwich, c.1825.

It is believed that Francis Molton was an Italian and that his surname was anglicised from the Italian surname of Moltoni. Francis Molton was recorded as a weather-glass maker at St Laurence Steps, Norwich in 1810, but a barometer signed Francis Molton & Co., London is extant which can be dated to around 1800. He moved to Dove Street, Norwich in 1822 and remained there until at least 1843, described as an optician, barometer and thermometer manufacturer. He made high-quality stick and wheel barometers, some with shell inlay and some with the dial at the top of the case. On some wheel instruments he favoured a cogged spindle to adjust the set hand as seen in *Fig*. 112. The brass key below the case is connected to the cogged spindle which engages a cogwheel that turns the set hand. No other maker appears to have adopted this method. The theory of Molton's Italian origins is strengthened by the fact that his premises in St Laurence Steps were taken over by an Italian clock and watch maker, George Rossi, in 1822 when Molton moved to Dove Street. Rossi also made or sold barometers.

5

Later Italian Makers

The Bregazzi family originated in northern Italy. Their village of Stazzona lies in the hills above Dongo, a township on the western shore of Lake Como in Lombardy. The family can be traced back to 1676 when Domenico Bregazzi was born. His grandson Andrea had three sons; the eldest was Domenico, born 1780, and the second son was Samuel born in 1782. It is known that the family was related to Gioacchino Antonio Rossini, the composer.

The two sons may have been the first members of the family to migrate to England, where Samuel is recorded in 1809 as 'S. Bregazzi & Co., Willow Row, Derby. Barometer maker'. The '& Co.' probably refers to his elder brother Domenico, who became an artist and exhibited at the Royal Academy of Arts in 1811.

The brothers probably left Italy very early in the nineteenth century when many young men emigrated to avoid the war being waged by Napoleon. It is thought that Samuel may have served an apprenticeship in the craft of gilding before leaving Italy, or stayed in London to learn the trade before settling in Derby. Samuel married in 1810 and had seven children; John, the eldest, worked for his father and when his father died in 1841 he was only 20, so his mother continued the business with John's help. John married in 1847 and started a business in Corn Street, but he died in 1863 and the business was sold.

Samuel made stick and wheel barometers, and *Fig.* 113 shows a wheel instrument of his with the case veneered with finely grained mahogany. A Fahrenheit alcohol thermometer is fitted to the dial and the shape of the case suggests that it was probably made as a companion to a longcase clock. In 1830 he produced for a customer a combined clock, barometer and thermometer in the form of a church tower of Gothic structure. The round dial barometer was set in an extravagantly carved oak case shaped to look like the tower of All Saints' Church, Derby (now the Cathedral). Samuel worked in Queen Street Derby from 1816 (see *Fig.* 115).

Around 1820 a second group of Bregazzis left Stazzona and made their way to England to avoid military conscription when Austria occupied Lombardy after the defeat of Napoleon. Two of these, Innocent and Peter Bregazzi, were half-brothers of Samuel, and it is believed that they worked for him before setting up in partnership in Nottingham as carvers, gilders and barometer makers in 1825. Their advertisement is shown in *Fig.* 116. Innocent returned to Stazzona in 1835, but Peter continued the business into the 1840s when he sold it to relatives Crosta & Co., the partners being

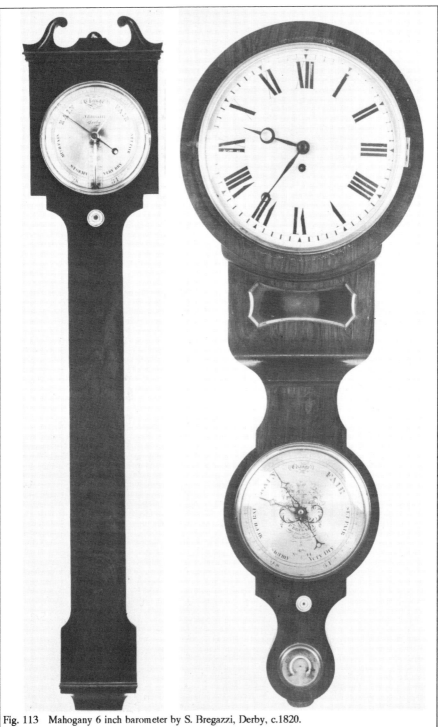

Fig. 113   Mahogany 6 inch barometer by S. Bregazzi, Derby, c.1820.
Fig. 114   Rosewood clock/barometer by P. Bregazzi, Nottingham, 1843.

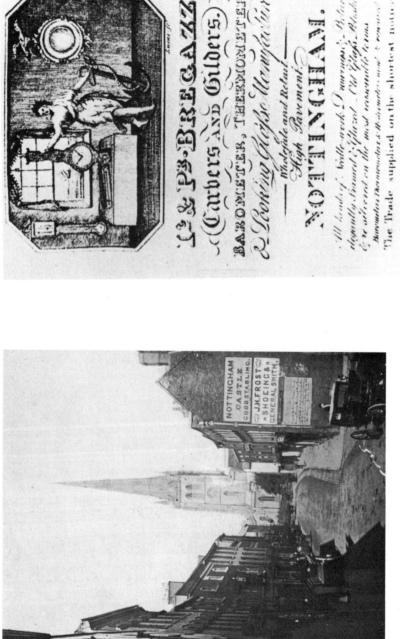

Fig. 116 Advertisement of Innocent & Peter Bregazzi, c.1830
(City of Nottingham Public Library).

Fig. 115 Queen Street, Derby, c.1870 where Samuel Bregazzi traded
(Derby Museum, Derby).

Crosta, Gobbi and Cetta, who remained there until 1860.

Fig. 114 illustrates a clock and barometer by Peter Bregazzi in a case veneered in rosewood. The clock has an eight-day fusee movement with an anchor escapement and the pendulum can be seen through the glass below the 12 inch face. A circular Fahrenheit thermometer with a pear-shaped reservoir is incorporated at the bottom of the case. The barometer has an 8 inch silvered dial with leaf scrolls and the Royal Coat-of-Arms. It is signed P. Bregazzi, Patentee, Nottingham, No. 44. There is also an English diamond Design Registration Mark showing that it was registered at the British Patent Office. These marks are found on nineteenth-century furniture from 1842 to 1883 and from the letters and figures the date of the barometer can be calculated; in this case, 25 September 1843.

Pastorelli is another well-known name connected with instrument making. Fortunato Pastorelli appears to have been the first member of the Pastorelli family to arrive in Britain; he is recorded as working in the Hatton Garden area of London between 1805 and 1830 when he was succeeded by his son Anthony, who was at 40 Cross Street from 1830 to 1849. His son Francis then took control and continued the business at various addresses until 1897. *Fig.* 117 shows a mahogany cased barometer with kingwood banding by Fortunato Pastorelli at 4 Cross Street, Hatton Garden. It is 46 inches high, 13 inches wide and the clock has a pendulum. It has the usual additional instruments, including a detachable thermometer and hygrometer. Another Pastorelli barometer is shown in *Fig.* 118, this time by Joseph Pastorelli, London, from another branch of the family. It is a particularly elegant 10 inch dial barometer with scroll pediment. Joseph Pastorelli was an important maker whose son followed him in the business.

The well-known firm of Pastorelli & Rapkin was formed in 1872 by the amalgamation of two businesses: Francis Pastorelli & Co. of 7 Great Warner Street and Alfred Thomas Rapkin of 61 Hatton Garden. The two businesses were consolidated into one at larger premises at 46 Hatton Garden in 1873 where it remained well into the twentieth century. Francis moved from 208 Piccadilly to 10 New Bond Street in 1878 and remained there until 1897; this was a separate business and not a part of the partnership. A solid walnut stick barometer by Francis Pastorelli is shown in *Fig.* 119, made at 208 Piccadilly where he was working between 1856 and 1878 as an optical, mathematical and philosophical instrument maker. This type of barometer was popular during the last quarter of the nineteenth century; they mirrored the Gothic or medieval influence which was revived during the late Victorian period. The cases were variously carved in solid oak, walnut, mahogany or rosewood with differing shaped pediments and cistern covers. Alfred Pastorelli, another member of the family who was working as a barometer and thermometer maker from 1884, joined the partnership in 1894.

Another group of Pastorellis settled in Liverpool. It is believed that Josh. Pastorelli, who made the barometer illustrated in *Fig.* 120 at 47 Alberon Street, Liverpool, came to Liverpool from Italy with his uncle around 1800 and that his uncle eventually moved to London. The barometer illustrated is unusual in that the door is hinged from the left side of the case and there is a key on the right side to adjust the vernier.

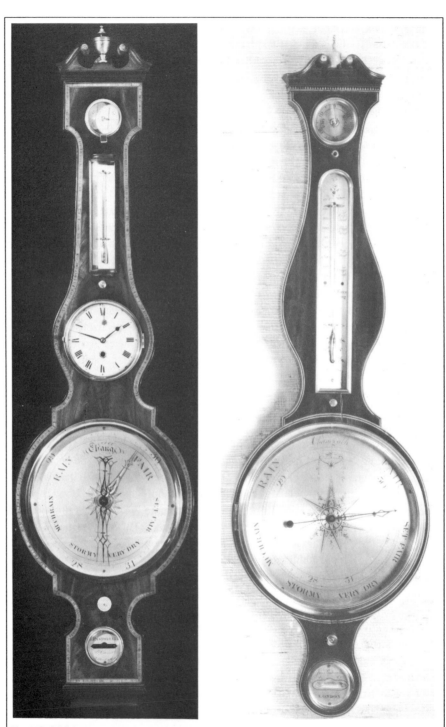

Fig. 117 Mahogany 11 inch barometer by F. Pastorelli, London, c.1830 (*Stair & Co. Ltd, London*). Fig. 118 Mahogany 10 inch barometer by Joseph Pastorelli & Co., London, c.1805 (*Stair & Co. Ltd, London*).

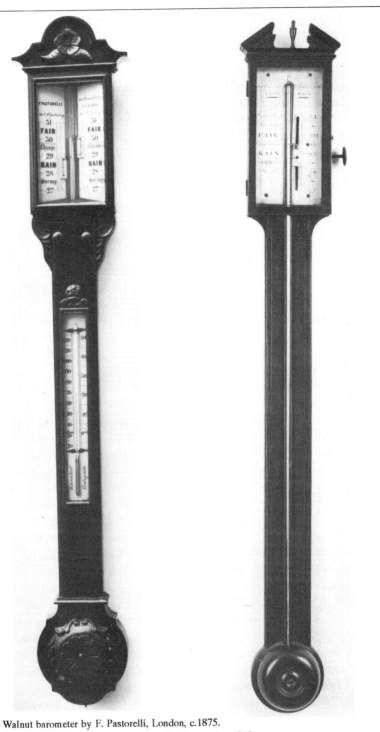

Fig. 119   Walnut barometer by F. Pastorelli, London, c.1875.
Fig. 120   Mahogany barometer by Josh. Pastorelli, Liverpool, c.1810.

The Pastorellis were related by marriage to the Casartellis and it is said that Josh. Pastorelli trained Lewis Casartelli in barometer making before Lewis set up in business on his own account in Liverpool in 1812. The Casartelli family came from Tavernerio, a few miles east of Como, so it is reasonable to assume that Tavernerio was also the home of the Pastorelli family. Josh. Pastorelli was succeeded by his son John in 1837 at Cable Street, and he was in business in Liverpool for 20 years as an optical instrument maker. He made stick and wheel barometers, and portraits of him and his wife Sarah, who was a Scot, are shown in *Figs* 121 and 122.

Edward Cetti, whose trade card is shown in *Fig.* 123, was in partnership with a Pastorelli at 11 Brooke Street, London in 1852. He came from Careno on Lake Como, which was also the home of the Zambra family. In 1853 he took control of the business and traded as Edward Cetti, barometer and thermometer maker, until 1870 when he took a son, also Edward, into partnership.

The trade card was used between 1876 and 1879 and the 'Late J. Tagliabue' refers to John Tagliabue who was working at 11 Brooke Street early in the century. Edward senior returned to Italy in 1890 when his son continued the business in Brooke Street until 1895; then his son, also called Edward, carried on until 1898. Edward senior had two other sons, for whom he started a furnace glasshouse.

A plain traveller's or mountain barometer made by E. Cetti & Co. is illustrated in *Figs* 124 and 125. It is in a brass case with a rotating milled rim and pointer set at 29.7 inches. There is no separate altitude scale so it would be necessary to refer to 'Airey's Tables' to determine heights. Professor Airey was the Astronomer Royal in the 1840s and produced a table showing barometer readings from 31 to 19.959 inches with the corresponding heights from 0 to 12,000 feet.

A Joseph Cetti, who was working at 54 Red Lion Street, Holborn, was probably a relative. He was an early migrant to London from Careno on Lake Como, who is recorded as a looking-glass, barometer and print maker. The case decoration of the barometer by him in *Fig.* 126 is unusual in that flower head inlays are used each side of the thermometer instead of a complete flower arrangement or fan inlay as used previously. The large shell inlay at the base of the case is also an unusual feature.

The Italian John Kalabergo was born in Lombardy in 1812, but little is known of his movements until 1832 when he set up in business in the Market Place, Banbury as a watch, clock and barometer maker and jeweller. He traded as a licensed hawker No. 286B and was well known in the area for his clocks and numerous Sheraton shell barometers.

In 1850 he visited Italy and brought back his nephew Giovanni Kalabergo to help in the shop. The nephew was apparently temperamental and impetuous and they often quarrelled. In 1852, while visiting customers in the Priors Marston area, the nephew shot his uncle on Williamscote Hill. Giovanni was tried, found guilty of murder and publicly hanged in Oxford, the last public hanging to take place in the city. The grave-stone of John Kalabergo is in St John's Churchyard, Banbury, and friends erected a memorial stone on Williamscote Hill 'to their highly esteemed townsman', which is now in Banbury Museum.

Fig. 121   Portrait of John Pastorelli (*Julie Gill, Liverpool*).

Fig. 122   Portrait of Mrs John Pastorelli (*Julie Gill, Liverpool*).

Fig. 123   Trade card of Edward Cetti & Co., London, c.1875 (*D. Carrington, Horsham*).

Fig. 124   Pocket barometer with 1.75 inch dial by E. Cetti & Co., c.1875 (*Dario A. Fumolo, London*).
Fig. 125   Reverse side of barometer in Fig. 124 (*Dario A. Fumolo, London*).

102

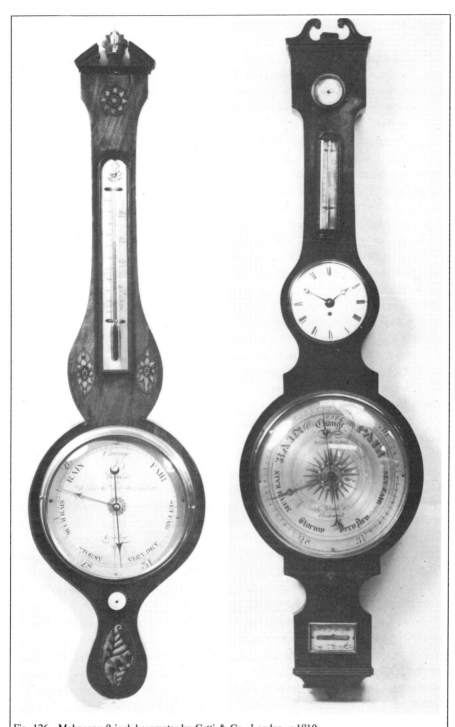

Fig. 126 Mahogany 8 inch barometer by Cetti & Co., London, c.1810.
Fig. 127 Rosewood 12 inch barometer by D. Fagioli & Son, London, c.1840 (*Patric Capon, London*).

Dominic Fagioli was a prolific Italian maker of wheel barometers. He started in Gt Warner Street, London in 1834 and took his son into partnership in 1839. It ended in 1853. Barometers signed 'J. Fagioli, Gt Warner Street' are extant and this could have been the son who continued on his own after the partnership ended. Some barometers were decorated with mother-of-pearl and others were painted to simulate inlay, but *Fig.* 127 shows a rosewood instrument with an eight-day clock made by father and son.

The barometer in *Fig.* 128 is signed 'C. Gerletti, Glasgow'. Charles Gerletti is recorded as a looking-glass manufacturer in Saltmarket, Glasgow from 1828 to 1848 when he was succeeded by Dominick Gerletti, probably his son, who also advertised himself as a carver and gilder, optician, picture frame maker and firework artist. The barometer illustrated is identical to barometers made in London at this time so that it is more likely to have been made by one of the London makers.

J. Laffrancho of Ludlow was the only maker of barometers of the design shown in *Fig.* 129. The mechanism is the same as in other wheel barometers except that the thread connecting the pulley to the glass weights is some 22 inches long. The mirror has a flat glass and its position near the base of the barometer brought it down to a convenient height to be used as a mirror. Laffrancho also made the normal type of scroll pediment barometer and, earlier, the Sheraton shell broken pediment barometer. Another rare barometer, this time with a carved and gilt oak case, was made by J. & L. Pini & Co. of Brooke Street, Holborn, London around 1855 (*Fig.* 130). Shaped leaf scroll borders decorate the case with a pear forming the pediment. The thermometer is housed in a brass box. Joseph and Luigi Pini worked at 23 Brooke Street between 1848 and 1862 as barometer and thermometer makers, carvers and gilders.

A prolific maker in the West Country was John Baptist Giobbio who, in 1829, was a founder member and senior warden of the Trowbridge Masonic Lodge, in Wiltshire. He came from Lodge 24, probably Devizes Lodge, and his membership ceased in 1838. He made scroll pediment wheel barometers and a large number of Sheraton shell instruments (see *Fig.* 131); these invariably have masonic signs and symbols engraved on the dial. It appears that Giobbio had shops in the adjacent towns of Trowbridge and Devizes, as his address is rendered variously as 'Trowbridge & Devizes' or else the towns singly on different barometers. A few barometers are signed 'Giobbio & Co.'. The angle barometer by him in *Fig.* 133 is very unusual because the angle arm is from the left of the upright frame. A round cover shields the bulb cistern tube but the register plates are not protected by glass; this allows the set pointer to be manually operated along the bar above the tube.

Louis Bellatti of Grantham preferred to use boxwood cistern tubes for his angle barometers and one by him is shown in *Fig.* 132. The case is veneered with finely grained mahogany and the silvered register plates are protected by a glazed door which has two hinges along the top of the arm and opens upwards; this is to allow the manual adjustment of the indicating pointer which runs along a metal bar below the tube. The cistern has a hemispherical cover and the portable screw can be seen.

The Bellatti family were jewellers from an area north of Milan, most probably

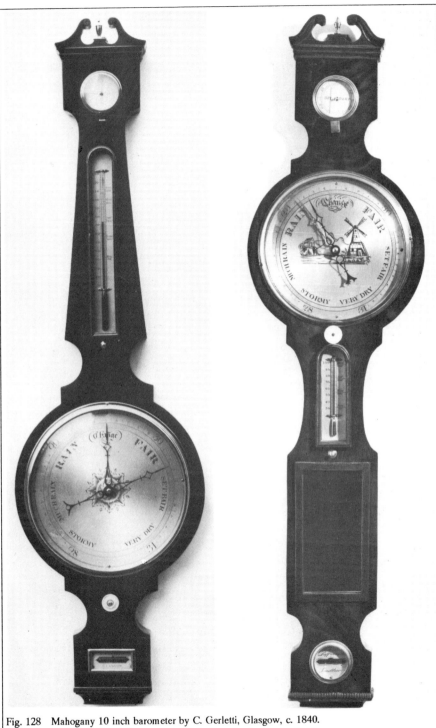

Fig. 128   Mahogany 10 inch barometer by C. Gerletti, Glasgow, c. 1840.
Fig. 129   Mahogany 8 inch barometer by J. Laffrancho, Ludlow, c.1845.

Fig. 130 Oak 8 inch barometer by J. & L. Pini & Co., London, c.1855 (*Sotheby's, London*).
Fig. 131 Mahogany 8 inch barometer by Giobbio, Trowbridge, c.1820.

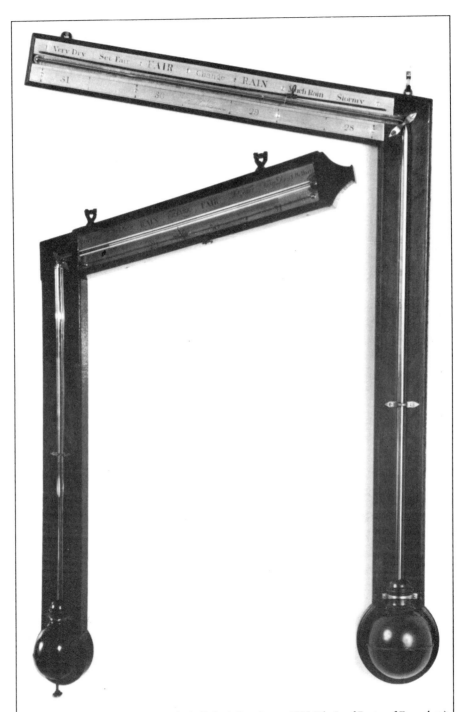

Fig. 132 Mahogany angle barometer by L. Bellatti, Grantham, c.1825 (*The Lord Boston of Faversham*).
Fig. 133 Mahogany angle barometer by Giobbio, Trowbridge & Devizes, c.1820 (*Walker & Walker, Hungerford*).

Como, and Louis is said to have come overland on foot to England from Como very early in the nineteenth century as he married an English girl, Sarah Stokes, at Wulfram's Church, Grantham in 1810. They had six children. He was in business in Westgate, Grantham as a barometer maker and in 1819 advertised that he had 'fitted up a new Machine which will enable him to execute all orders, either manufacturing or repairing, or for blowing glass for different experiments, on the shortest notice'; also that he 'will attend every week at Mr Manton's, gunmaker, Stamford where all orders from the neighbourhood are requested to be sent, and will have prompt attention.'

In 1821 he moved to High Street, Grantham and advertised that he 'has just returned from London with a variety of Optical, Mathematical and Philosophical Instruments and is enabled to execute all orders on the shortest notice.' He was noted for his angle barometers, also the Sheraton shell type of wheel barometer. In the High Street he also sold and repaired clocks and watches and became unpopular with his local competitors as he accused them of inefficient repair work. He sometimes styled himself Dr Bellatti but his rivals called him Dr Quack.

In 1834 he advertised that he was selling up and leaving the country, and a six-day auction sale followed. He was not long abroad as he was advertising again from Cornhill, Lincoln in 1835; he soon moved to Silver Street, Lincoln and concentrated on barometers and other optical instruments.

Louis died in 1840 and his eldest son, also Louis, who was born in 1816, entered into an arrangement with a William Chapman, a local clock and watch maker, who advertised that 'he had made an engagement with Mr Louis Bellatti, eldest son of the late Mr L. Bellatti, whose experience for several years in the Watch manufactories of London, Coventry and other parts and the instruction he received in the Optical and Philosophical department with his late father will enable William Chapman to execute all branches.' The son was working on his own by 1842 in Steep Hill, Lincoln as a watch and clock maker and remained in business at various addresses in Lincoln until he died in 1893.

Charles Bellatti was the elder brother of Louis senior and was born in Como, Italy about 1782. He appears to have set up in business in Burton-on-Trent, where he is known to have made barometers of the Sheraton shell type, and later moved to Stodman Street, Newark where he took his son Charles into partnership around 1830; they traded as Charles Bellatti & Son and sold 'the most improved types of Wheel, Upright and Diagonal Barometers together with many other instruments'. It appears that father and son split up in the 1840s as Charles senior was on his own at Lombard Street, Newark in 1851, described as a carver and gilder, but there is no record of his son in the census of that year. Charles senior died in 1872.

Bolongaro is another well-known Italian name in the field of instrument making. The name can be traced back to 1310 when the family lived in Sinigaglia; they were a noble and powerful family, which settled in Stresa on Lake Maggiore. The Villa Bolongaro (the second property on the right in *Fig.* 134) was built around 1770 by Giacomo Bolongaro on his return from Germany where he made his fortune in business.

Dominic Bolongaro (pictured with his wife in *Figs* 135 and 136) was born in 1780

VEDUTA DI STRESA SUL LAGO MAGGIORE.

Alla nobil Donna, la Signora Anna e Maria Bolongaro

Fig. 134 Stresa on Lake Maggiore, Lombardy, Italy *(M.F. Bolongaro, Cumbria)*.

in Stresa, and most likely came to Manchester around 1805, probably with Charles Joshua Ronchetti and Lewis Anthony Casartelli. He worked for various employers, including Baptist Ronchetti and Vittore Zanetti, before setting up on his own in 1817 as a carver, gilder, looking-glass and picture frame maker; he was also an optician, made barometers and sold prints and oil paintings.

A barometer by him is shown in *Fig.* 137. The moulded case is veneered with mahogany, and a hemispherical cistern cover is used for the boxwood cistern. The silvered brass register plates are enclosed by a hinged glazed door and the overall height is 37.5 inches. The finial is missing.

In 1848 Dominic took his son Peter into partnership with the firm name of Dominic Bolongaro & Son. The business expanded and in 1855 they acquired the shop next door, 30 Market Street, where they were described as 'Print sellers and publishers to the Queen; carvers, gilders, barometer and thermometer makers, artists' colourmen and picture restorers'. Dominic died in 1856 and Peter successfully continued the business until he retired in 1888 when it was sold. He died in 1892.

The Peduzzi family was mentioned in chapter 2 when James Butterworth described Anthony Peduzzi's shop in Manchester early in the nineteenth century. A barometer signed Joseph Peduzzi & Co., Manchester is shown in *Fig.* 138. Joseph was, no doubt, a member of the family and, like Anthony, also made well-finished and tastefully decorated instruments. The case is veneered with mahogany giving a herring-bone pattern and the register plates are attractively engraved with a leaf and flower spray.

Serafino Antonio Maria Calderara came from Italy to London in 1820 and initially made household and industrial thermometers. By 1831, he was described as a barometer, thermometer and philosophical instrument maker and made a variety of wheel barometers, including those with mother-of-pearl inlay. He was assisted in the business by his two sons Serafino and Alfred James, and when their father died in 1874 the name of the business was changed to Serafino & Alfred Calderara. While still making barometers, the brothers specialised in making thermometers and hydrometers for the brewery trade, as well as instruments for laboratory furnishers specially made to order.

Serafino died in 1896 and A.E. Calderara, the son of Alfred, joined the business. Alfred died in 1911 when his son carried on the business until it was merged with Short & Mason Ltd in 1935. A.E. Calderara was a founder member of the British Lampblown Scientific Glassware Manufacturers' Association in 1917. He was the Association's first honorary treasurer and held that office until 1947; from 1927 to 1947 he was vice-president except for the year 1936 when he was President. In 1948 he was elected a life and honorary member of the Association in recognition of his long and valuable services; he remained an honorary member of the Council until his death in 1958.

The name of Comitti is recorded on barometers that were made early in the nineteenth century. Joseph Comitti of Banff, Scotland made Sheraton type wheel barometers, with the classic shell marquetry, around 1820 and he also made stick instruments with bulb cisterns. A stick barometer signed Geronimo Comitti in the Sheraton style is also extant. However, the most important member of the family was

Fig. 136　Portrait of Ellen Bolongaro, née Turner (*M.F. Bolongaro, Cumbria*).

Fig. 135　Portrait of Dominic Bolongaro (*M.F. Bolongaro, Cumbria*).

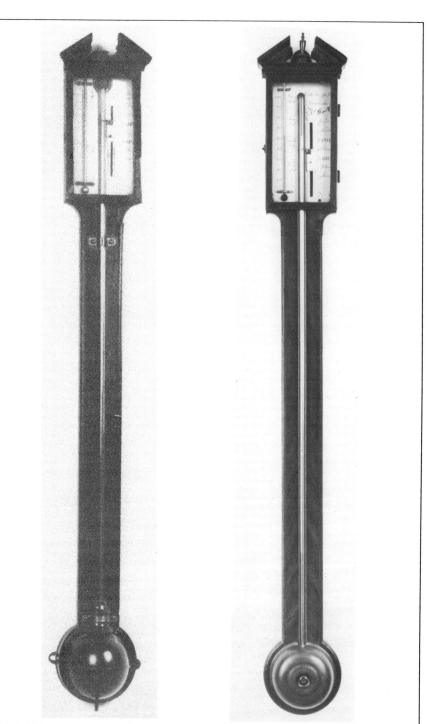

Fig. 137 Mahogany barometer by Dominic Bolongaro, Manchester, c.1830 (*M.F. Bolongaro, Cumbria*).
Fig. 138 Mahogany barometer by Josh. Peduzzi & Co., Manchester, c.1830.

Onorato Comitti, who appears to have come to London from around Lake Como, Italy about 1840, probably to join other members of the family already here. He is recorded as working for John Cetta in Back Hill, Holborn in 1841 and with Negretti & Zambra at 1 Hatton Garden in 1861.

In 1870 Onorato set up in business on his own at 2 Back Hill, Holborn. He had three children; for the birth of the first two, who were boys, he took his wife back to Italy, but by the time the third was due, a daughter called Clementine, the family appears to have become sufficiently anglicised as she was born in St Pancras, London. One of the sons, Luigi, became a partner in 1878 when the name was changed to O. Comitti & Son, and it was Luigi who incorporated the business in 1898 as O. Comitti & Son Ltd. In the 1890s the business advertised itself as patentees of the 'Visible' aneroid barometer (*Fig.* 139) and sole manufacturer of the Torricelli barometer.

The daughter Clementine married into the Barker family, and on the death of Luigi the business moved to this family, by whom the business is still being run under the Comitti name. Around 1900 the company expanded into making clocks and a catalogue dated 1910 offered over 75 different clock designs, well over a hundred different barometers, barographs, thermographs etc. and a vast range of thermometers for almost every conceivable application. The company appears to have made barometers continuously for at least 122 years. They are still making wheel, stick and marine barometers and barographs today, being reproductions of popular nineteenth-century instruments (*Figs* 140–142).

The name of Casartelli was associated with barometer making very early in the nineteenth century, but probably reached its greatest fame later in the century. The Casartelli family, in common with other notable barometer makers, came from Tavernerio, a few miles east of Como, where they were long established as land and property owners and makers of thermometers and hygrometers. Lewis Anthony Casartelli was born in 1784 and migrated to Manchester around 1805 with Charles Joshua Ronchetti his cousin. He worked for several instrument makers before setting up in business on his own in Liverpool in 1812 as a barometer and thermometer maker. He did work for the famous scientist Dr John Dalton, who formulated the table of atomic weights, and advised Lewis that he would make his fortune if only he learned to speak English properly. An unusual bow-fronted barometer signed 'L. Casartelli, Liverpool' is shown in *Fig.* 143 with a vernier and silvered register plates. The front of the case is veneered with well-figured wood in three vertical sections and the cistern cover shape is uncommon.

Lewis retired and returned to Italy in 1845 when the business was taken over by two relatives, Anthony and Joseph. They were in partnership until 1852 when Joseph left and moved to Manchester to marry Harriet Ronchetti and take over the business of John B. & Joshua Ronchetti who were her brothers. Anthony continued the Liverpool business, with other members of the family, until well into the twentieth century.

Joseph Casartelli expanded the Manchester business into optical, mathematical, philosophical and engineering instrument makers and photographers, and was elected a member of the Manchester Literary and Philosophical Society in 1858. The business was in Market Street, and around 1875 he was advertising:

Fig. 139   Watch-sized barometer with 1.75 inch open dial in leather case, c.1870.

Fig. 140   Mahogany barograph from the catalogue of O. Comitti & Son Ltd, London, 1992.

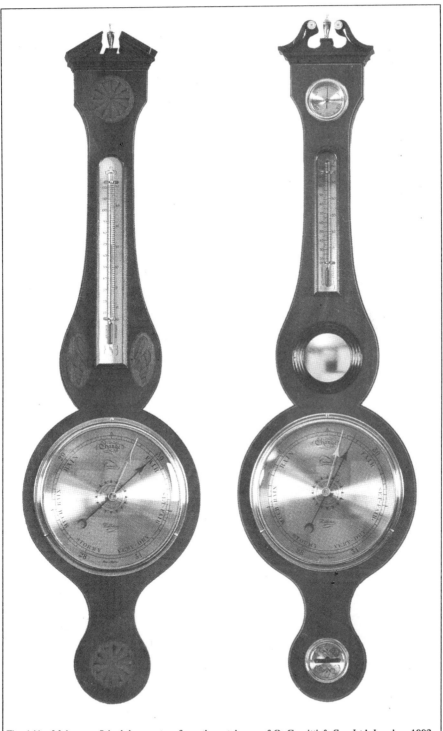

Fig. 141   Mahogany 8 inch barometers from the catalogue of O. Comitti & Son Ltd, London, 1992.

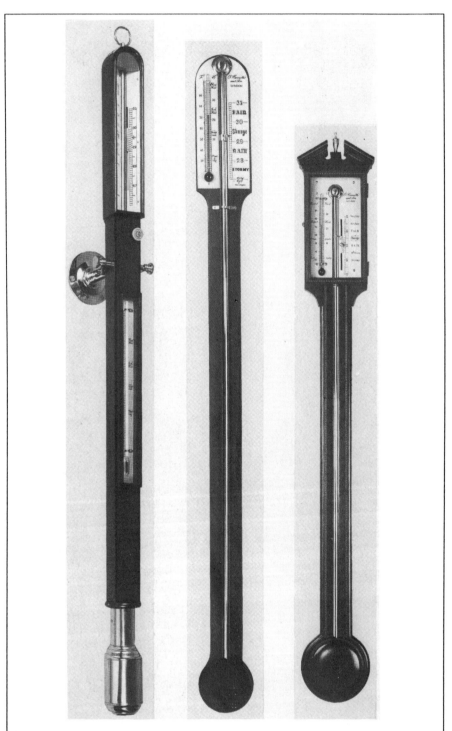

Fig. 142   Barometers from the catalogue of O. Comitti & Son Ltd, London, 1992.

116

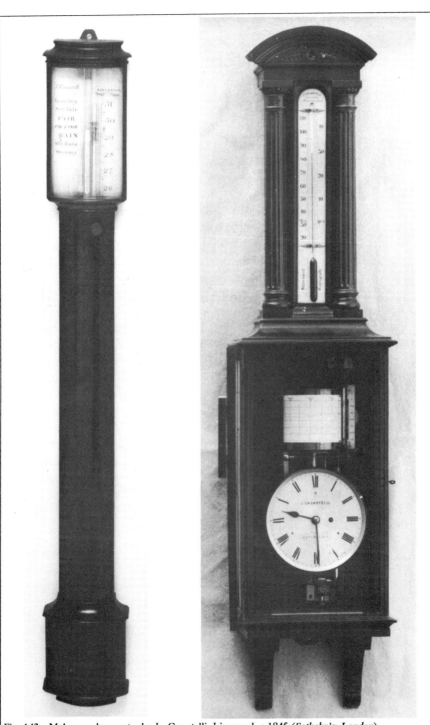

Fig. 143 Mahogany barometer by L. Casartelli, Liverpool, c.1845 (*Sotheby's, London*).
Fig. 144 Mercury barograph by J. Casartelli, Manchester, c.1870 (*Peter D. Bosson, Wilmslow*).

117

Best carved upright portable Barometers in oak, mahogany or walnut, 2 indices, compensated for capacity, ivory plates and finished in the best manner. Best circular or Wheel Barometers, 2 indices, of the best quality, guaranteed to work well. Commoner sorts if required. Best Standard Aneroid, or Portable Barometers, with altitude scale. Casartelli's Registering Barometer, with Clock.

By the 'Registering Barometer, with Clock' was probably meant Casartelli's modification of the Milne barograph which a few meteorological instrument makers, including Negretti & Zambra and L. Casella of London, had begun to make for sale to the public. Casartelli's instrument is shown in *Fig.* 144. It comprises a large diameter siphon tube, with a counterpoised float attached to a chain passing over a wheel carrying a recording pencil which, by suitable mechanism, is brought once every hour in contact with ruled paper, mounted on a drum revolved by clockwork. The clock is rewound weekly when a fresh paper is attached to the cylinder and the series of dots impressed on the paper shows the height of the mercury every hour of the day or night. The case is of oak and the clock has an anchor escapement with a pendulum and fusee movement.

A smaller and more efficient barograph was developed around 1885; an example by J. Casartelli & Son is shown in *Fig.* 145. It operates on the same principle as the aneroid barometer in that the expansion and contraction of a series of vacuum chambers is transmitted by levers to a pointer. The pointer has a pen attachment which moves over a chart wound round a drum which, activated by clockwork, rotates round its vertical axis once every seven days; the chart remains attached to the drum by a metal strip. The pen leaves behind it a continuous visual record of all pressure changes, and the record produced is called a barogram. The instrument is housed in an attractively carved oak case and there is a drawer for storing the charts. The clockwork has an eight-day movement and is wound up by removing the top of the drum which exposes the winding key and adjustment lever. The barometer has a porcelain dial and the indicating hand is operated by a spring and levers connected to the pen arm near the fulcrum.

In 1888 the Casartelli business was describing itself as:

The oldest and most important firm of its kind in Manchester and indeed has no equal outside London. The firm have secured gold and silver medals for the excellence of workmanship and accuracy of construction and results, and have been found worthy of the highest words of commendation.

The name was changed to J. Casartelli & Son when Joseph Henry, the son of Joseph, joined the business in 1896; Joseph died in 1900 and his son carried on until his death in 1925. In 1917 Joseph Henry was a founder member of the British Lampblown Scientific Glassware Manufacturers' Association.

The very rare and interesting traveller's barometer in *Fig.* 146 is signed 'Joseph Casartelli & Son, Manchester. Watkin Patent No. 773'. It is contained in a brass case with a diameter of 3 inches and has a depth of 1.5 inches. The silvered brass dial is calibrated down to 26 inches on three concentric circles so that the indicating hand

Fig. 145 Oak barograph by J. Casartelli & Son, Manchester, c.1900 (*Peter D. Bosson, Wilmslow*).

Fig. 146 Traveller's barometer with 3 inch dial by Joseph Casartelli & Son, Manchester, c.1915 (*Steven Henriques, Richmond*).

119

would have to complete a full circle three times to record a change of pressure from 26 to 31 inches; this allows the scale to be divided into fiftieths of an inch. There is an aperture in the dial to indicate which circuit is in use, by the figures I, II or III. The altitude scale from 0 to 5,000 feet is similarly calibrated on the three concentric circles and is in steps of 10 feet. Both scales are fixed but there is a very ingenious pointer which turns with the milled rim bezel; the pointer extends to the middle of the dial and is attached to the arbour housing by a spring.

Louis Casella was another important instrument maker whose name is still synonymous with barometer making today. Louis was born in Edinburgh in 1812. His father, almost the youngest of a family of seventeen, was a musician, artist and writer, and had come to England to better himself. He succeeded, it seems; he married one of the 'three beautiful Miss Ramsays' and eventually became tutor to the daughters of George III.

The son Louis was apprenticed to Cesare Tagliabue, an optical instrument maker in London; and in 1837 he married Tagliabue's eldest daughter, Marie Louise, and was taken into partnership in 1838 as Tagliabue & Casella.

Not all the instruments offered for sale by the partnership were made in England; some were bought from Barella, Valleggia and Grimoldi of Amsterdam, Reballio of Rotterdam and Sala of Leiden. Fairly frequent visits were made to the Continent for buying and selling. A cash book entry for £6 14s 4d in 1837 was for expenses during five days visiting Leiden, Haarlem, Amsterdam and Rotterdam.

Cesare Tagliabue died in 1844 when the name was changed to L. Casella. The business continued to flourish and Louis became well known, with customers who included Darwin, Livingstone and Galton. Casella also designed and made equipment for explorers Burton, Speke, Halleur and Lord Shomberg Kerr. He also supplied equipment for medical research, including the first clinical thermometer. By about 1850 Casella had probably become the leading meteorological instrument maker in Europe, if not the world. The catalogue cover shown in *Fig.* 147 gives an indication of the regions of the world where trade was conducted.

L. Casella supplied the full range of domestic barometers. *Fig.* 148 shows two instruments from the Casella catalogue of c.1875 which demonstrate the carved cases which became popular in the 1870s. These barometers were available in rosewood, walnut, oak and mahogany, either plain or elegantly carved to any style of furniture or architecture, for halls, libraries etc. Stick or pediment barometers for general household purposes were also offered. One in a plain solid oak case by Casella is shown in *Fig.* 149. It was described in the catalogue as a 'portable barometer, plain pattern, thermometer in front, ivory plates, rackwork, and vernier reading to the 100th of an inch, portable screw and plate glass. Price £2 10s 0d.' They were also available in rosewood and mahogany.

In 1857 L. Casella produced an agricultural, gardener's or cottage barometer (*Fig.* 150). It was designed as a cheap, light and portable barometer for use in cottages, garden sheds, greenhouses and farm buildings and cost 12s 6d. The one illustrated is made of solid mahogany with printed paper plates protected by glass. There is a manual setting ring and below the weather indications is the word 'Compensating'. This indicates

AN ILLUSTRATED

AND

DESCRIPTIVE CATALOGUE OF

SURVEYING,

PHILOSOPHICAL, MATHEMATICAL,

OPTICAL, PHOTOGRAPHIC,

AND

STANDARD METEOROLOGICAL

INSTRUMENTS,

MANUFACTURED BY

L. CASELLA,

SCIENTIFIC INSTRUMENT MAKER

To the Admiralty,

BOARD OF TRADE, BOARD OF ORDNANCE, THE GOVERNMENTS AND OBSERVATORIES OF INDIA, RUSSIA, SPAIN, PORTUGAL, THE UNITED STATES, AND THE BRAZILS;

THE BRITISH METEOROLOGICAL AND THE ROYAL GEOGRAPHICAL SOCIETIES, THE ROYAL OBSERVATORIES AT KEW, CAPE OF GOOD HOPE, AND OF THE WAR DEPARTMENT;

THE UNIVERSITIES OF CAMBRIDGE, OXFORD, AND LONDON;

THE LEADING HOSPITALS AND INFIRMARIES; AND THE OBSERVATORIES OF ARMAGH, WASHINGTON, VICTORIA, TORONTO, CALCUTTA, THE MAURITIUS, ETC. ETC.

INTERNATIONAL EXHIBITION,
1862.
THE ONLY PRIZE MEDAL AWARDED
FOR
REGISTERING METEOROLOGICAL
INSTRUMENTS.

147, HOLBORN BARS, LONDON, E.C.

Removed From 23, HATTON GARDEN.

received 28/1/1871

Fig. 147   The cover of the catalogue of L. Casella, c.1863.

Fig. 148 Carved barometers from the catalogue of L. Casella, London, c.1875.
Fig. 149 Oak barometer by Casella, London, c.1860 (*D. Birt, Canada*).

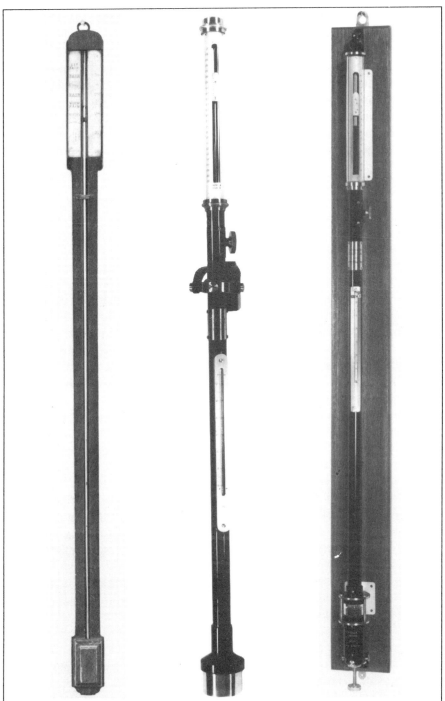

Fig. 150   Agricultural mahogany barometer by L. Casella, London, c.1860.
Fig. 151   Modern Kew pattern marine barometer by Casella London Ltd, Kempston, Bedford, 1992.
Fig. 152   Modern Fortin barometer by Casella London Ltd, Kempston, Bedford, 1992.

that the inch calibrations on the register plates are, in fact, slightly less than inches to compensate for the slight rise or fall in the level of the mercury in the bulb cistern, as the height of the mercury ranges between 26 and 31 inches on the scale.

The *Cottage Gardener* of 27 October 1857 commented that the cottage barometer 'Would adorn alike the gardener's cottage or the hall of a mansion. We are much obliged to Mr Casella for thus popularising these useful instruments. His name is a guarantee for the character of any instrument.' *The Field* of 7 November 1857 wrote: 'Casella's cottage barometer has lately been brought under our notice, very much to our delight and profit. They have registered with unerring faithfulness the recent changes in the weather.'

Casella gained considerable expertise in marine instruments. *Fig.* 151 shows a design of Kew pattern marine barometer that was being made at the turn of the century and is still being made today. The barometer tube projects into a stainless steel cistern through a supporting unit which incorporates a protective cover for the cistern and also a gland. The glass tube is firmly held within a cylindrical brass case, which has two slots at the top for viewing the meniscus and for carrying the setting device and vernier. The scales are protected by an outer glass cylindrical sleeve. *Fig.* 152 shows a Fortin barometer still being made today by Casella London Ltd. It is almost identical to the Negretti & Zambra instrument shown in *Fig.* 168 (chapter 6), but the cistern has been improved; it consists of three parts: a transparent brass cylinder with a brass top, a brass cylindrical base and a pliable wash-leather bag. A large adjusting screw at the bottom of the base allows the centre of the wash-leather bag to be raised or lowered so that the mercury level can be set to the zero point. This is an ivory pointer inside the cistern, fixed rigidly to the cistern top.

A barometer made specially for surveyors and mining engineers by Casella, London is shown in *Fig.* 153. The barometer fixed scale range is from 26.5 to 34 inches, which allows a movable altitude scale range from 4,000 feet above sea level to 2,000 feet below sea level. The pressure scale is divided into twentieths of an inch and the height/depth scale is calibrated in steps of 20 feet, but with the help of the rotating magnifier it is possible to read up to two-hundredths of an inch on the barometer scale and to 4 feet on the altitude scale. This type of barometer was sold for £6 in 1875 with an extra 10s for the stout leather case, lined with velvet, and sling strap.

Two sons of Louis, Louis Marino and Charles Frederick, joined their father in the business and the three worked together until Louis died in 1897. Charles then took charge as his brother had developed other interests, and the business was incorporated in 1910 under the name C.F. Casella Ltd. The company, now known as Casella London Ltd of Kempston, Bedford, still makes, among many other instruments, Kew pattern and Fortin barometers; also display, small pattern and open-scale barographs very similar to those made a hundred years ago.

L. Casella was in competition with Negretti & Zambra in the barograph market from the 1860s; the company still offers three different models of barograph to suit the needs of professional and amateur meteorologists, schools and universities. Two of the models illustrated in *Fig.* 154 are of traditional appearance with glazed wooden cases and polished brass pillars, linkages and fittings. The other is more functional looking, having stove-enamelled base and acrylic cover.

124

Fig. 153   Surveying barometer with 41/2 inch dial and magnifier by Casella, London, c.1890.

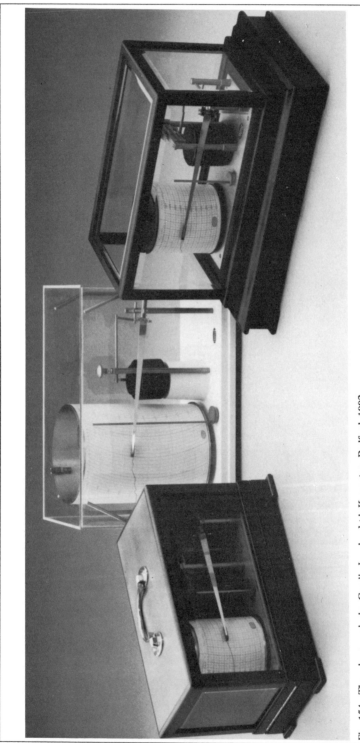

Fig. 154 Three barographs by Casella London Ltd, Kempston, Bedford, 1992.

6

The Partnership of Negretti & Zambra

The earliest Negretti on record is Antonio. His son, Jacopo, was a painter born in Serinalta, near Bergamo in Lombardy, northern Italy, who died in Venice in 1528. The name first appeared on barometers in Britain at the end of the eighteenth century as Negretti & Co., Plymouth, c.1790, followed by Negretti, Bristol, c.1820 and Gaeton Negretti, Manchester, c.1840.

Henry Negretti (*Fig.* 155) is the best-known member of the family in England. He was born in Como, northern Italy in 1818 and came to this country when he was 12 years old. In 1838 he was apprenticed to F.A. Pizzala as a journeyman in his trade as a glassblower, and the Articles of Agreement show that he was to be paid £1 15s per week for one year. For this he undertook to:

> Diligently and faithfully serve him according to the best and utmost of his power, skill and knowledge of the said trade or business and in all things whatsoever in anywise relating thereto and obey and execute the orders of him and shall not nor will divulge and make known the secrets of the said Francis Augustus Pizzala whether in or relating to the said trade or business or his family or other concerns whatsoever and will be true just and honest.

By 1840 Negretti was working on his own in Hatton Garden as a barometer and thermometer maker, and between 1841 and 1844 he assisted Jane Pizzi, the widow of Valentino Pizzi. In 1845 he was on his own at 19 Leather Lane; and in 1850 he went into business with Joseph Warren Zambra, forming the renowned partnership of Negretti & Zambra.

Negretti made the headlines in 1865 when a fight between some Englishmen and Italians took place in the billiards room of The Golden Anchor in Saffron Hill, London. An Englishman, Michael Harrington, was stabbed to death and Serafino Pellizzioni, a picture frame maker from Como, was convicted of his murder and sentenced to death at the Old Bailey. Henry Negretti believed that he was innocent and organised a committee to defend him. They uncovered new evidence and brought a private prosecution for murder against Gregorio Mogni, a cousin of Pellizzioni. Mogni pleaded guilty and was sentenced to five years' imprisonment; Pellizzioni was released. When Henry Negretti died in 1879, his obituary in *The Times* read: 'A man of great talent and almost indomitable energy and perseverance, he was equally distinguished for his

Fig. 156   Joseph Warren Zambra, 1822–97.

Fig. 155   Enrico (Henry) Angelo Ludovico Negretti, 1818–79.

uprightness of character and his open and gentle manners, which endeared him to all who had dealings with him; among the Italians he enjoyed an almost patriarchal popularity.'

Negretti's partner, Joseph Warren Zambra, was the son of Joseph Cesare Zambra, who was mentioned in chapter 2 as an itinerant barometer seller. He was born in 1796 in Careno on the east shore of Lake Como; and at about the age of 20 he left the building trade in Careno and came to London where he was employed by Joseph Cetti as a traveller in barometers and other goods. His round included parts of Essex where he met Phillis Warren, the daughter of James Warren, a butcher and farmer of Sewers Farm. He later started his own business in Saffron Walden and in 1821 he married Phillis Warren.

A son, Joseph Warren Zambra (*Fig.* 156) was born in 1822. When he was 18 the family moved to 23 Brooke Street, Holborn, London where the father continued in business. Joseph Pini was already trading from this address. In 1847 the son formed a partnership with John Tagliabue at 11 Brooke Street, but this cannot have lasted long as the partnership with Henry Negretti began in 1850.

The partnership was signed on 24 April 1850; it was an equal partnership and they undertook 'to be just and faithful to each other' and 'not to employ or discharge from their employ any clerk or servant without the consent of the other partner'. Another clause stated:

That neither of the said partners shall give credit to any but regular customers of the said partnership and that if either of the said partners shall give credit to or disburse any sum or sums of money for any person whosoever exceeding the sum of ten pounds without the consent of the other partner in writing first obtained then that partner shall stand alone to the loss hazard and adventure thereof and the share of the said partner in the general profits of the said business shall stand charged.

The Negretti & Zambra partnership seems to have prospered from the outset and soon gained a good reputation both in Britain and abroad. The first bound cash book of the business, covering the period 26 August 1853 to 2 October 1855, makes very interesting reading. It shows the extent of the business after they had been trading for little more than three years. The partners visited the Continent on more than one occasion and purchased supplies or instruments from Paris, Bentheim, Magdeburg and Vienna. Most of the items from Paris were probably aneroid barometers.

The records show that they were supplying the following Italian makers in London during the period: Tagliabue, Ortelli, Dubini, Pini, Casella, Pizzalla, Ronketti, Amadio, Rivolta, Pastorelli, Bernasconi, Cetti, Gally, Colombo, Grimoldi and Barelli. Outside London, the following Italians were customers: Bregazzi, Derby; Riva, Weymouth; Tagliabue, New York and Negretti & Leoni, New York. The Negretti in this partnership was Gaetano Negretti, an elder brother of Henry Negretti.

Notable English makers in London supplied were: E.G. Wood, Carpenter &

Fig. 158 Hatton Garden, London, the original premises of Negretti & Zambra.

Fig. 157 Old Leather Lane, London, the site of Henry Negretti's first enterprise in 1843.

Westley, Horne & Thornthwaite, Smith & Beck, Spencer Browning & Co., Wither-spoon & Gaudin, Imray, Lejeune & Perkins, W.E. & F. Newton and Frith of London, Liverpool and Sheffield. Outside London, the following English makers were customers: Braham, Bath; Dixey, Brighton; Chadburn, Liverpool; Abraham, Liverpool; Henry Frodsham, Liverpool; Dancer, Manchester; J. Davis & Son, Derby; Gardner, Glasgow; Lennie, Edinburgh; Spears & Co., Dublin; Mason, Dublin; and Yeates, Dublin.

The firm also supplied instruments to Prince Albert, The Royal Observatory at Greenwich, Washington Observatory, Toronto Observatory, the Admiralty, the East India Company and the boards of Ordnance, Trade and Health. The Kew Committee, Lea & Perrins and the Buckingham Lunatic Society were among their other customers. The cash book shows that goods were sent to 61 cities and towns in England; to Edinburgh, Glasgow, Aberdeen and Dundee in Scotland; and to Belfast, Dublin and Londonderry in Ireland. Exports were made to New York, Ontario, Malta, Milan, Poona, Bombay, Sydney, Hamburg and Valparaiso.

In 1851, only a year after forming the partnership, they exhibited a variety of instruments at the Great Exhibition in the Crystal Palace. These included a standard open cistern barometer, a self-registering barometer and a pocket sympiesometer. The firm received the only prize medal award for meteorological equipment and were appointed Meteorological Instrument Makers to Queen Victoria.

In the early days of the partnership several patents were granted to the firm covering improvements in the design and construction of meteorological and philosophical instruments. The fame of the instruments grew; and they were officially approved by the Royal Observatory, the British Meteorological Society, government departments and the armed services (see the cover of their catalogue in *Fig.* 159). Their equipment became standard for travellers and explorers, being carried to the poles, taken to great depths in the oceans and lifted to the remarkable height, in 1862, of seven miles in a balloon.

A balloonist's barometer by Henry Negretti, made when he was trading on his own at 19 Leather Lane, is shown in *Fig.* 160. It has an ivory scale which is calibrated from 31 to 5 inches and can be adjusted by turning the ivory key half-way up the tube. This is necessary to zero the scale by ensuring that the brass arm, connected by a brass rod to the bottom of the scale, is level with the mercury in the short limb. A Gay-Lussac tube is used and the bulge in the lower section of the long limb contains a Bunten air trap.

The vernier only covers the normal scale of 27 to 31 inches which suggests that its main purpose was to record sea level air pressures. However, as the scale is graduated down to 5 inches, it can record altitudes of up to 40,000 feet – almost eight miles. It was probably used for early balloon experiments, since Henry Negretti was an acquaintance of James Glaisher, the well-known balloon pioneer. It is known that Glaisher compared two of Negretti & Zambra's aneroid barometers with a siphon tube mercury barometer at pressures down to 7 inches, and this could well have been the barometer that was used. Glaisher made numerous risky flights by hot-air balloon and on one flight, while testing the composition of the air at 37,000 feet, was almost

AN

ILLUSTRATED

DESCRIPTIVE CATALOGUE

OF

OPTICAL, MATHEMATICAL, PHILOSOPHICAL,

PHOTOGRAPHIC

AND

STANDARD

METEOROLOGICAL

INSTRUMENTS,

MANUFACTURED AND SOLD BY

NEGRETTI AND ZAMBRA,

OPTICIANS AND METEOROLOGICAL INSTRUMENT
MAKERS TO

HER MAJESTY THE QUEEN, H.R.H. THE PRINCE CONSORT,

THE ROYAL OBSERVATORY, GREENWICH;
THE ADMIRALTY; HON. BOARD OF ORDNANCE; BOARD OF TRADE; THE
BRITISH METEOROLOGICAL SOCIETY;
THE OBSERVATORIES, KEW, TORONTO, WASHINGTON, VICTORIA;
THE EAST INDIA GOVERNMENT;

PHOTOGRAPHERS TO THE CRYSTAL PALACE, SYDENHAM.

No. 1, HATTON GARDEN, 107, HOLBORN HILL,

ALSO;

59, CORNHILL,

LONDON, E.C.

PRICE TWO SHILLINGS AND SIXPENCE.

Fig. 159   The cover of Negretti & Zambra's catalogue, c.1863.

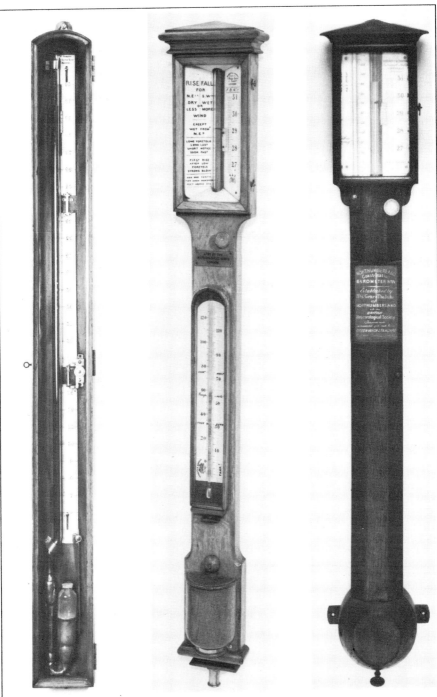

Fig. 160   Mahogany balloonist's barometer by H. Negretti, London, c.1845.
Fig. 161   Oak sea-coast barometer by Negretti & Zambra, London, 1858 (*Science Museum, London*).
Fig. 162   Oak sea-coast barometer by Negretti & Zambra, London, c.1860 (*Sotheby's, London*).

asphyxiated.

The storm barometer, also known as the sea-coast or life-boat station barometer, can be attributed to Negretti & Zambra. Admiral Robert Fitzroy was Secretary of the Lifeboat Association and he was concerned that fishermen and others, whose lives could be endangered by sudden changes in the weather, should have the benefit of access to a barometer. His persistence persuaded the Board of Trade in 1858 to provide, at public expense, a fishery or sea-coast barometer in many fishing villages and towns, fixed in a prominent position, so that anyone wishing to consult it could do so.

Fitzroy developed this type of barometer in conjunction with Negretti & Zambra. *Fig*. 161 shows barometer F.B. No. 2 which was issued to the St Ives Coast Guard Station in 1858. The frame is of solid oak with a strong tube of very large bore. It has a portable cistern, single vernier and porcelain register plates protected by a glazed door. The Fahrenheit thermometer scale and the register plates are signed 'Negretti & Zambra's Patent, 11 Hatton Garden & 68 Cornhill, London'.

When other makers began to produce similar barometers, Negretti & Zambra inserted a warning in their catalogue to 'caution the Public against purchasing cheap and worthless imitations of Fishery barometers as leading to disappointment. Full details both as to construction and use of the true Fishery instrument will be found in Negretti & Zambra's Barometer Manual, compiled by Admiral Fitzroy for the Board of Trade.'

Following the example of the Board of Trade, the Royal National Lifeboat Institution supplied each of its stations with a similar barometer, while the Duke of Northumberland and the British Meteorological Society erected several on the coast of Northumberland. These were also made by Negretti & Zambra and one is illustrated in *Fig*. 162. The case is of solid oak with a circular cistern cover and chamfered pediment. The ceramic register plates are signed 'Negretti & Zambra, Instrument Makers to Her Majesty, London' and, with the thermometer tube, are protected by a glazed door, but the bulb of the thermometer is below the door and partly covered by a metal box. The trunk is inset with a glass plaque inscribed 'Northumberland Coast-Station Barometer No. 14. Established by His Grace The Duke of Northumberland and the British Meteorological Society. Barometer reads one hundredth of an inch below Greenwich Standard. Sept. 1860. James Glaisher F.R.S.'

Admiral Fitzroy wrote of the success of the sea-coast barometers in his report from the Meteorological Office to the Board of Trade in 1864:

In my last report I stated how highly the Board of Trade 'Fishery' Barometers have been valued on the coasts. They are now 80 in all, specially lent, under due control and care. Two only of this number have become slightly defective, and have been exchanged. Not one has been injured in carriage, singular to say, between Cornwall and the Shetland Isles, Ireland and Yorkshire. It may be more readily estimated mentally than accurately proved, to what extent these simple instruments (all reliably made and tested) have already been the means of saving life and property. Explanatory manuals and blank forms for diagrams have been extensively circulated among the coasters and fishermen, who are all, now, much influenced by, and very thankful for, the benefits of this Act of their Government. Many are local instances of similar beneficence by individuals – especially the Duke of Northumberland, who has placed no less than 14 barometers.

Another specialised type of barometer made by Negretti & Zambra was the farmer's barometer shown in *Fig*. 163. It has a portable cistern tube in a solid oak case and there is a sliding vernier. Admiral Fitzroy's weather indications are used on the porcelain register plates and there are two mercury thermometers used in conjunction to make a wet and dry bulb hygrometer – the farmer needed more than most people to be able to forecast the weather accurately and an oat-beard hygrometer has only a limited effective life. The plates on this barometer are signed 'Farmers Barometer. Patent No. 612. Negretti & Zambra. Opticians to Her Majesty. 1 Hatton Garden, E.C., 122 Regent St, W., and 59 Cornhill, E.C., London'. Similar farmer's barometers were made for about 50 years; some had carved oak frames and ornamental mountings and some had ivory register plates.

Negretti & Zambra also made miner's barometers, such as the one shown in *Fig*. 164. It has a stout oak frame and the porcelain plates and vernier are covered with a glass window. The scale is calibrated from 26 to 33 inches so that the barometer can be used at least 2,000 feet above or below sea level. Miner's or pit barometers were on sale from the early 1860s and the government became so convinced of the advantages of using a barometer at mines that the Mines (Coal) Regulations Act 1872 included the following: 'After dangerous gas has been found in any mine, a barometer and thermometer shall be placed above ground in a conspicuous position near the entrance of the mine.' Records kept had shown that before an explosion in a coal mine there is a reduction in the air pressure.

Negretti & Zambra were also involved in the development of the marine barometer. Marine barometers differed from ordinary stick barometers in having a section of the tube below the plates restricted in diameter to prevent or contain the oscillation of the mercury during a storm. Marine barometers are always mounted on gimbals fixed through holes a short distance below the register plates.

Marine barometers with wooden frames continued to be made into the last quarter of the nineteenth century, but an improved design was developed around 1855 by John Welsh of the Kew Observatory. It was called the Kew pattern marine barometer and was accepted by the Board of Trade and became the standard issue by the Board to the British Marine. Admiral Fitzroy, however, considered that this barometer was too delicate in construction, difficult to read and likely to be broken by the firing of the ship's guns, so he set out to improve it in association with Negretti & Zambra. *Fig*. 165 shows an example of a marine barometer taken from their *Treatise on Meteorological Instruments* dated 1864. The tube is fixed to a boxwood cistern which is plugged with very porous cane at the top to allow the ready influence of variations in air pressure on the mercury. The frame and all fittings are of brass and the tube is packed

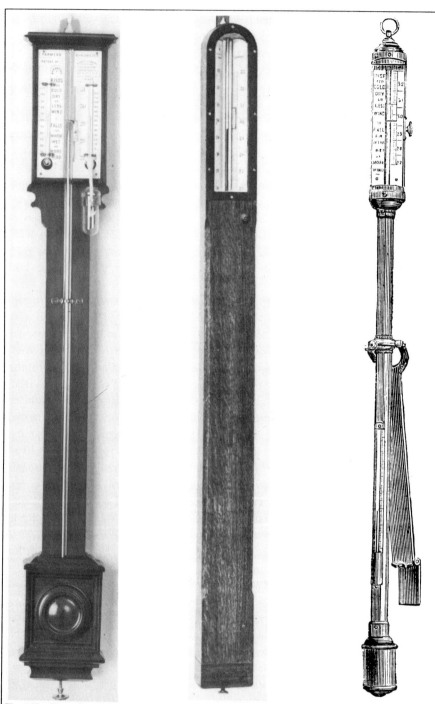

Fig. 163 Farmer's oak barometer by Negretti & Zambra, London, c.1865 (*D. Birt, Canada*).
Fig. 164 Miner's oak barometer by Negretti & Zambra, London, c.1875.
Fig. 165 Fitzroy marine barometer by Negretti & Zambra, London, c.1865.

with vulcanised india rubber. Porcelain is used on the register plates and a thermometer is attached to the lower section of the case with the bulb enclosed within the frame next to the tube.

Experiments were carried out to compare the Kew pattern barometer and one embodying Fitzroy's improvements. On one occasion the two barometers were placed in close proximity to the heaviest guns of HMS *Excellent*, fired under the direction of Captain Hewlett, with Henry Negretti present. When the smoke had cleared, the instruments were examined. It was found that the concussion had shattered the Kew barometer, but the improved barometer was not only intact it was operating in a perfectly normal manner. Further tests established that the new barometer could stand up to the most severe concussion that a modern man-o'-war could create. It was named the Fitzroy marine barometer and was manufactured by Negretti & Zambra.

Fig. 166, taken from Negretti & Zambra's catalogue of 1878, shows (second from the left) a marine barometer with a sympiesometer fitted. These were used in conjunction with a marine barometer if very accurate and comparative observations were required. For marine use, of course, the tube of the sympiesometer had to be contracted to prevent oscillation.

Negretti & Zambra's expertise in the specialised barometer market received a boost in 1862 when the partnership took over the business of John Frederick Newman, an English optical, mathematical and philosophical instrument maker in London from 1816. Newman was one of the leading makers who had been developing barometers with greater accuracy to satisfy the demands of scientists. He had made standard and portable barometers for the Ross Antarctic expedition and his meteorological station barometers were installed throughout the British Empire. He also developed in 1833 a portable iron cistern which avoided the use of a leather base as he considered that leather was not sufficiently durable.

From the Newman barometers, Negretti & Zambra developed the standard Kew type barometer which was generally adopted by meteorologists. An example is given in *Fig.* 167, mounted on an oak board for station use. The upper end of the case has two vertical openings opposite each other so that readings can be taken aided by light reflected from the white opaque glass reflector let into the board. The tube has a cast-iron cistern and manually operated vernier from the milled screw below the register plates.

Negretti & Zambra also made standard Fortin type barometers, or standard barometers on Fortin's principle, which was another attempt to improve the accuracy of the scientific barometer, named after Nicolas Fortin, who suggested combining a glass cistern with a leather base and an ivory point to determine the zero of the scale. A Fortin type barometer, similar to the Kew type barometer in *Fig.* 167, is illustrated in *Fig.* 168, except that the cistern is formed from a glass cylinder so that the level of the mercury can be seen. A conical length of ivory is fixed to the top of the inside of the cistern with the point of the cone facing downwards. The point is set to coincide exactly with the zero of the scale and before taking a reading the mercury in the cistern is raised or lowered by the adjustable screw, operating against the leather base, until

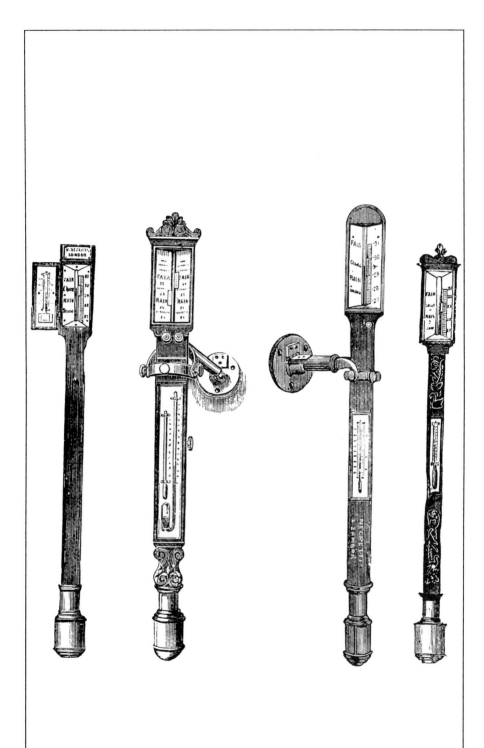

Fig. 166   Four marine barometers from Negretti & Zambra's catalogue, 1878.

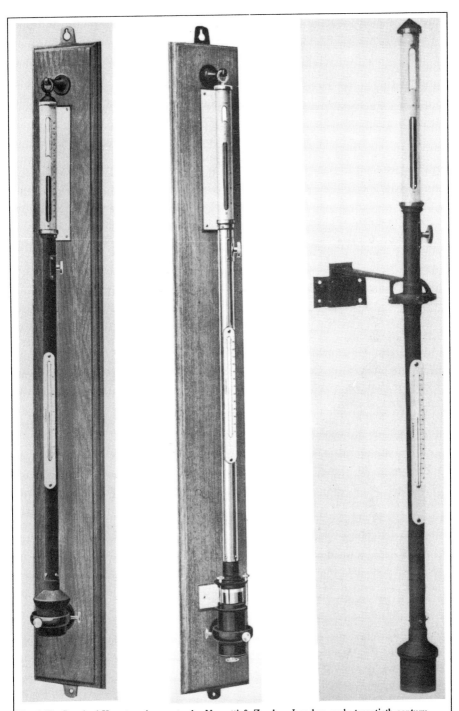

Fig. 167   Standard Kew type barometer by Negretti & Zambra, London, early twentieth century.
Fig. 168   Standard Fortin type barometer by Negretti & Zambra, London, early twentieth century.
Fig. 169   Standard Kew type marine barometer by Negretti & Zambra, London, early twentieth century.

it just touches the point of the ivory. This system allows a very accurate reading to be taken and was adopted and retained with little alteration until today.

Fig. 174 (below) illustrates a Fortin type mountain barometer made by Negretti & Zambra. It has an extended scale calibrated down to 25 inches and could be used for measuring heights of up to 5,000 feet. The instrument could be made portable by adjusting the screw at the base of the cistern and they were sold with a brass tripod stand and travelling case.

A standard Kew pattern marine barometer made by Negretti & Zambra, London early in the twentieth century is illustrated in *Fig.* 169. It is similar to the standard Kew type barometer shown in *Fig.* 167 except that it is mounted on a gimbals, rather than a board, and the bore of the tube is contracted between the register plates and the cistern so that the movement of the mercury is restricted. These barometers were supplied in a deal varnished box with a lock and key and rope handles.

The Kew pattern marine barometer shown in *Fig.* 170 was made by Negretti & Zambra, London around 1940 and is engraved 'Barometer Marine Mark II Ref. Met. 1542'. It was supplied to the Meteorological Office and has a Meteorological Office number, which reveals that it was returned to the makers for servicing and checking in 1944, 1954 and 1958. It has a 'Gold Slide' fitted to the frame instead of the usual thermometer. This was a device invented in 1914 by E. Gold of the Meteorological Office, London and comprises a thermometer built into a type of slide rule. Its use is to provide easy adjustment for latitude, height of the cistern above sea level and index error. There are various patterns of Gold Slides. This one was made by Negretti & Zambra, London around 1940, and its own numbering system shows that it was checked and serviced in 1945, 1952, 1956 and 1964. The barometer is in its original carrying case of varnished deal with a lock and key, rope handles and rubber interior fittings. Marine barometers were normally supplied in these boxes.

An interesting glycerine and mercury long-range barometer, developed by Negretti & Zambra in the 1880s, is shown in *Fig.* 171, with an oak case and a mercury thermometer at its base. A siphon tube is used with the closed end about 33 inches long and the other only a few inches in length; to this short end is joined a glass tube of much smaller diameter so that both limbs are the same length with the smaller one being open at the top. The large tube, which is behind the porcelain register plate and cannot be seen, is filled with mercury, and the small tube, which is broken, is partly filled with glycerine. Due to the unequal capacity of the two tubes and the difference in the specific gravity of mercury and glycerine, the scale is extended over 24 inches or eight times a normal mercury scale. It sold for three guineas.

It is clear that the few Italian barometer makers who diversified into non-domestic barometers, such as marine, station and mountain instruments, played a very important part in their development. Negretti & Zambra, in particular, had a good working relationship with Admiral Fitzroy and with James Glaisher, and this gave them a distinct advantage in the development of marine barometers and those for measuring altitudes.

Although Negretti & Zambra made their name by specialising in non-domestic instruments, they nevertheless supplied domestic instruments to retailers up and down

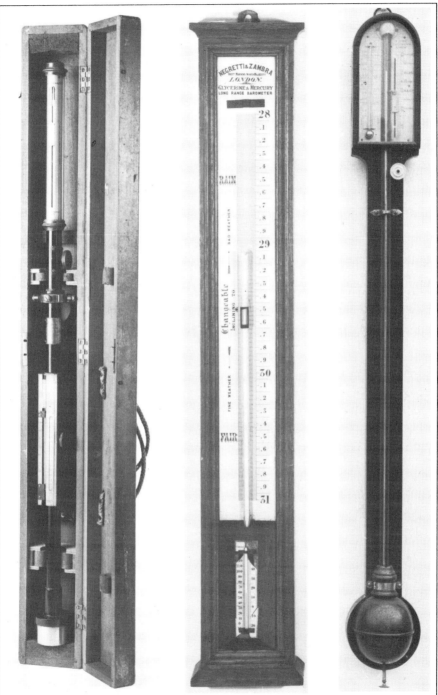

Fig. 170   Kew pattern marine barometer with Gold Slide by Negretti & Zambra, c.1940.
Fig. 171   Glycerine and mercury barometer by Negretti & Zambra, London, c.1885.
Fig. 172   Rosewood barometer by Negretti & Zambra, London, c.1850.

the country. The ivory register plates of the instrument in *Fig.* 172 are engraved 'W. Lund, 23 & 24 Fleet Street, London', but we know that he was only the retailer as 'Instructions for the Barometer' by Negretti & Zambra are printed and pasted on the back of the case.

Negretti & Zambra did not neglect the wheel barometer market, and their catalogue of 1860 describes 11 different wheel barometers with a price range from £1 10s to £20. The 10 inch dial was advertised at 6 guineas; similar barometers with 12 and 14 inch dials were thought suitable for mansions, clubs and public halls. A 14 inch instrument was advertised at £20 and had an eight-day pendulum clock fitted between the dial and the thermometer. Six wheel barometers were illustrated in the catalogue with the preface that:

Barometers can be supplied to order of any style of architecture, so as to correspond with the furniture of libraries, halls, etc. or to drawing from design. Barometers are now mounted in so many varied styles, both plain and carved, that the following are given only as those being most in demand. N.B. Dial barometers required for transmission to distant parts, such as India and the colonies, should be ordered expressly, as in that case they will be furnished with steel stopcock, to render them portable more effectually than can be done by the old method of plugging the tube. These additions will enhance the price of each barometer by 7s 6d.

The Negretti & Zambra barometer shown in *Fig.* 173 would have been for sale at around £3. The case is veneered in walnut and the round moulded edging is restricted to the sides of the case. This type of barometer was sometimes fitted with two brass set hands with 'A.M. Today' engraved on one and 'P.M. Today' on the other so that twice daily comparisons could be made. The hands were controlled by two keys set below the dial.

In 1864 Negretti & Zambra advertised domestic stick barometers, or pediment barometers as they were then known, generally for household purposes as follows:

They are intended chiefly for 'weather glasses' and are manufactured to serve not only a useful, but an ornamental purpose as well. They are usually framed in wood, such as mahogany, rosewood, ebony, oak or walnut, and can be obtained either plain or handsomely and elaborately carved and embellished, in a variety of designs, so as to be suitable for private rooms, large halls or public buildings. The scales to the barometer and its attached thermometer may be ivory, porcelain or silvered metal.

Negretti & Zambra appear to have been the last commercial maker of angle barometers, and *Fig.* 175 illustrates the model that was being advertised during the last quarter of the nineteenth century. It was described in their catalogue as follows:

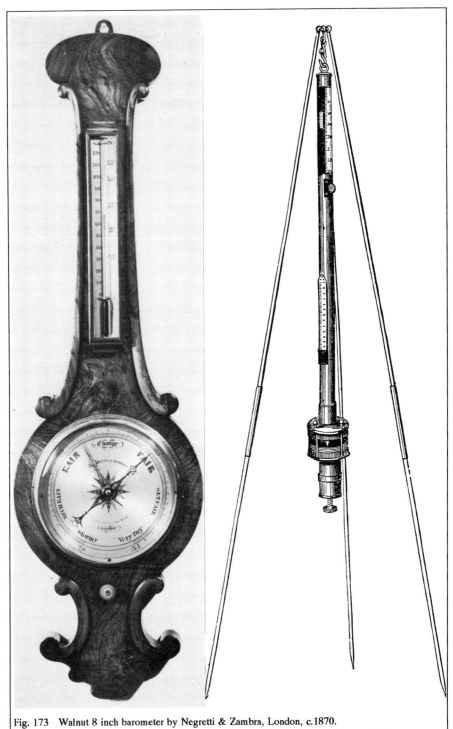

Fig. 173 Walnut 8 inch barometer by Negretti & Zambra, London, c.1870.
Fig. 174 Mountain barometer of Fortin type from Negretti & Zambra's catalogue, 1878.

143

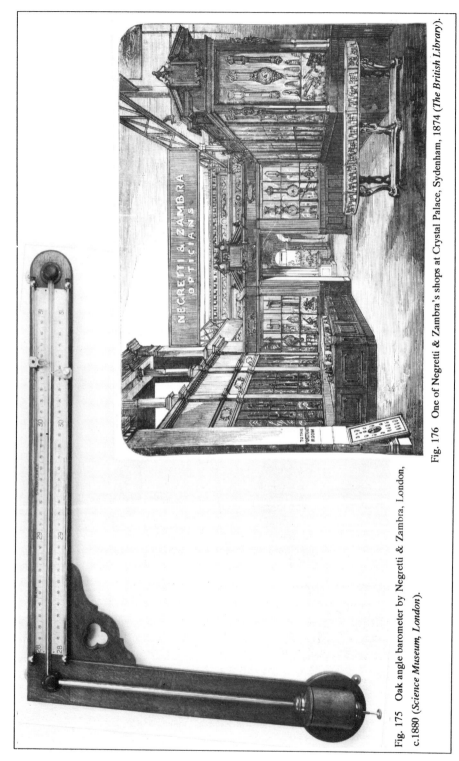

Fig. 175 Oak angle barometer by Negretti & Zambra, London, c.1880 (*Science Museum, London*).

Fig. 176 One of Negretti & Zambra's shops at Crystal Palace, Sydenham, 1874 (*The British Library*).

Diagonal Barometer: At the point on the vertical column where, in the usual barometer the 28 inches would be marked, the tube is bent at an angle and the remaining three inches of the scale viz. 29, 30, 31, are extended over a tube 36 inches long. The mercury moving diagonally travels over 12 inches of the tube for every inch on the vertical scale, adding to the interest of the instrument, as the slightest variations are thereby magnified, and are at once very noticeable, whereas they would be overlooked on the ordinary barometer. The tube is mounted on a stout well-made frame of oak or mahogany with engraved silvered metal scales, and with two setting indices. The instrument has a flexible cistern, and can be made portable for transport. Price £10.

Negretti & Zambra were also active in the development and production of the aneroid barometer, an instrument for measuring air pressure without the use of mercury. Lucien Vidie invented the first compact and truly portable aneroid barometer, but his patent expired in 1859 and Admiral Fitzroy, realising that the aneroid barometer could be of great benefit to sailors and travellers because of its portability, persuaded Negretti & Zambra to reduce its size so that it could be carried in the pocket. He also suggested improving its mechanical arrangement and compensation for temperature.

Negretti & Zambra undertook the necessary research, and in 1860 succeeded in producing a pocket barometer with an overall diameter of 2.75 inches and a depth of 1.75 inches. The compensation for temperature was carefully adjusted and the scale, which extended from 31 to 23 inches, was graduated under reduced pressure so that the dimensions were not quite equal, but more accurate. It had a silvered metal scale with a brass set hand and was advertised for sale at three guineas.

Fitzroy wrote of the pocket aneroid in his *Barometer Manual:*

> The aneroid is quick in showing the variation of atmospheric pressure ... it can
> be placed anywhere, quite out of harm's way, and is not affected by the ship's
> motion ... in descending or ascending elevations, the hand of the aneroid may
> be seen to move (like the hand of a watch) showing the height above the level
> of the sea, or the difference of level of places of comparison ... its convenient
> size and great sensibility, render it most useful for obtaining observations where
> a mercurial instrument is inconvenient to carry.

Negretti & Zambra continued to develop these barometers, and in 1861 marketed a watch-sized barometer identical to the one shown in *Fig.* 177. The overall diameter is less than 2 inches with a depth of little more than half an inch. A set hand has been dispensed with by substituting a small pointer; it is atttached to a milled rim which can be moved round the dial by hand and so indicate the last reading, which can be seen here at 29.7 inches. The instrument was intended for marine use as it has an enamel dial which is less likely to corrode. It has the usual adjusting screw at the back of the case, if it is necessary to adjust the reading when comparing it with a mercury barometer.

This type of barometer was also adapted for measuring altitudes and was sometimes

Fig. 177   Watch-sized barometer with 1.75 inch dial, c.1865.
Fig. 178   Pocket-sized barometer with 2.5 inch dial by Negretti & Zambra, London, c.1865.
Fig. 179   Pocket barometer with 2.75 inch dial by Negretti & Zambra, London, c.1875 (*Harold Judkins, Devizes*).

called the mountain aneroid. An illustration is given in *Fig.* 178 made by Negretti & Zambra around 1865. There are no weather indications, but the silvered brass scale extends down to 21 inches and there is an outer altitude scale from zero at 31 inches rising to 10,000 feet at 21.479 inches, in an anti-clockwise direction, in steps of 100 feet.

To use the instrument as an altimeter the milled rim is moved round until the small pointer is exactly level with the indicating hand; when the barometer is taken up an incline the indicating hand will move backwards, and from the difference between the pointer and the indicating hand the height of the climb can be calculated. To obtain an accurate measurement, two people should take simultaneous readings from two barometers, one at the bottom and the other at the top of the incline; this is because there could be a change in air pressure during the time that the climb takes place.

In 1862 Negretti & Zambra supplied two aneroid barometers to James Glaisher, the famous balloonist, for use on his noted scientific ascents of that year, the highest of which almost resulted in his death. Glaisher compared an aneroid with a mercury barometer at pressures down to 7 inches of mercury, which was an altitude of just over seven and a half miles, and found it to read correctly. In his *Travels in the Air*, Glaisher wrote: 'I have taken this instrument up with me in every subsequent high ascent.'

An interesting and rare barometer by Negretti & Zambra, London, is shown in *Fig.* 179. The silvered dial is engraved 'Whiteside-Cooks Sea Level Aneroid Patent No. 4424'. It has the usual milled rim carrying a small pointer round the dial, which extends down to 24 inches but, in addition, it has a second milled rim at the back of the brass case which can also be moved round. When moved, it carries with it the complete aneroid movement including the indicating hand. Round the side of the case there is an 'Ascent' scale going in a clockwise direction from zero to 6,000 feet and also a 'Descent' scale going in an anti-clockwise direction from the same zero to 1,400 feet. The scales are fixed and calibrated in steps of 20 feet and there is an engraved pointer on a movable rim.

To operate the barometer as an altimeter, the engraved pointer is set to zero on the side scale and the position then taken up by the indicating hand is recorded by adjusting the front milled rim until the small pointer is in line with the indicating hand. On making the ascent, the indicating hand will move in an anti-clockwise direction and the height can be ascertained by moving the indicating hand back to its original position, as shown by the small pointer, and reading off from the engraved pointer the movement in feet required to achieve this.

A specially commissioned and very attractive barometer by Negretti & Zambra is illustrated in *Fig.* 180. The barometer case is veneered with rosewood and is inlaid with exotic woods and ivory. Even the dial has veneer decoration and there is a church scene in ivory below it. 'Spring', 'Summer', 'Autumn' and 'Winter' foliage is depicted in the four corners around the dial and there are two wyverns facing a shield above the dial.

Towards the end of the century, few new barometer case designs appeared and

Fig. 180   Rosewood 8 inch barometer by Negretti & Zambra, London, c.1885 (*Brian and Angela Downes Antiques, Bath*).

Fig. 181   Mahogany barometer by Negretti & Zambra, London, c.1900 (*Christies, London*).

those that were made were based on the designs of earlier cases. An example is given in *Fig.* 181 made by Negretti & Zambra at the turn of the century. It is almost a reproduction of *Fig.* 47 (chapter 3), which was made some 80 years earlier, with the addition of inlaid decoration. The barometer could be described as late Victorian or Edwardian, but instruments continued to be made, based on earlier designs, in the twentieth century and they are still being made today.

A specially commissioned barometer made at the turn of the century by Negretti & Zambra, Opticians to the Royal Family, is shown in *Fig.* 182. It is in an oak frame and heavily carved with two griffins and trailing leaf scrolls. It was made for the Royal Yacht SS *Victoria and Albert* which was launched in 1899. Regrettably, the porcelain dial has been defaced by the old Ministry of Works broad arrow and serial number.

In 1915 Negretti & Zambra produced a forecasting aneroid barometer (*Fig.* 183) and patented a weather forecaster (*Fig.* 184). The barometer is 4 inches in diameter and sensitive to show the slightest change in air pressure; it also automatically gives the sea level reading at any altitude without the need to make any calculations. All that is necessary is to loosen the knob at the top of the instrument and revolve the back until the arrow on the side corresponds to the altitude at the place of observation; the knob should then be tightened and the hand of the aneroid will then indicate the present sea level reading.

The weather forecaster (*Fig.* 184) is 4.75 inches in diameter and comprises an outer brass ring on a stand and a brass disc within the ring which can be rotated by a small projecting handle at the back of the forecaster; there is a front brass disc that can be rotated by hand. The outer ring has a barometer readings scale in inches reduced to sea level and a wind direction scale, while the disc within the ring has 'rising', 'steady' and 'falling' wind indications which can be seen as the front disc is rotated. The forecasts were based on actual weather conditions noted over a period of ten years, and Negretti & Zambra claimed 292 correct forecasts annually or 80 per cent accuracy. The forecasting aneroid and the weather forecaster could be purchased separately or together, with the aneroid fitted in a velvet-lined pigskin case and the forecaster attached to the inside of the lid.

A pocket forecaster, in celluloid, with the forecasts on the back, was introduced by Negretti & Zambra in 1920 (*Figs* 185 and 186). The construction is similar to that of the forecaster in *Fig.* 184. Instead of a long aperture, the centre disc has three windows through which letters of the alphabet can be seen, and these represent 26 different weather forecasts listed on the back of the forecaster. Negretti & Zambra also produced a small model, 6 inches high, suitable for standing on a mantelpiece or desk. It was made of a metal casting, enamelled black, with silvered metal dial with black lettering. Negretti & Zambra also made pocket-sized forecasting aneroids, mounted with celluloid pocket forecasters on boards or bases, as shown in *Fig.* 187.

The weather foreteller by Negretti & Zambra in *Fig.* 188 was devised in response to customers who felt that if the weather forecaster were combined with a barometer in one instrument it would simplify its actual use. It is mounted in a polished oak frame, 10.5 inches in diameter, and has silvered dials and a glass front. It is simple to use;

Fig. 182 Carved oak barometer by Negretti & Zambra, London, c.1900 (*Negretti Automation, Aylesbury*).

Fig. 183 Forecasting barometer by Negretti & Zambra, London, c.1915 (*Dario A. Fumolo, London*).

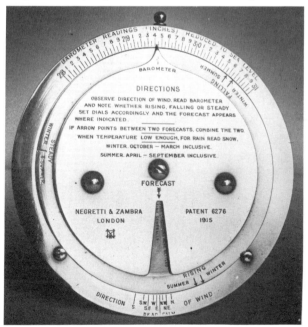

Fig. 184 Weather forecaster by Negretti & Zambra, London, c.1915 (*Negretti Automation, Aylesbury*).

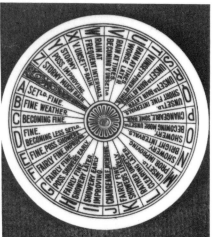

Fig. 185   Ivory weather forecaster by Negretti & Zambra, London, c.1920.
Fig. 186   Reverse side of weather forecaster in Fig. 185.

Fig. 187   Barometer and weather forecaster by Negrettti & Zambra, London, c.1920 (*Dario A. Fumolo, London*).

Fig. 188   Weather foreteller by Negretti & Zambra, c.1922 (*Dario A. Fumolo, London*).

Fig. 189   Pocket weather foreteller by Negretti & Zambra, c.1920.
Fig. 190   Side and rear view of weather foreteller in Fig. 189.

by setting the wind scale correctly and moving the gilt pointer to cover the barometer hand, the forecast at once appears in the metal window.

Another interesting combined barometer and weather forecaster by Negretti & Zambra is shown in *Figs* 189 and 190. It was called a weather watch or pocket weather foreteller and has a diameter of 1.75 inches. The front view shows the fixed wind scale at the bottom of the dial and the three windows 'Fall', 'Steady' and 'Rise' on the centre dial. On the back can be seen the 26 weather forecasts from A to Z, and on the side is the altitude scale from 0 to 3,000 feet, in steps of 25 feet, and the setting arrow.

In *The Field* magazine of 19 February 1938, Ernest Heath of Sennen in Cornwall wrote:

> I have a small local weather forecaster issued by Negretti & Zambra, which I bought in September 1924, and with which I have had 5,295 results. Of these 15 have been incorrect, equal to 0.2833 per cent; 412 have been partly correct, equal to 7.7809 per cent; and 4,868 have been correct, equal to 91.9358 per cent.

Negretti & Zambra's own claimed success rate of 80 per cent was raised by them to 90 per cent after extensive trials.

The partners alone seem to have pioneered and developed the weather forecaster, and in the 1920s, before there was a London Weather centre or even an Air Ministry roof in Kingsway, the source of weather information in the London daily newspapers was usually quoted as 'Messrs Negretti & Zambra' who were expected to offer comments on unusual weather conditions.

By 1864 Negretti & Zambra, like several other meteorological instrument makers, were making for sale to the public a modification of the Milne barograph, a self-recording mercurial barometer designed by Sir Alexander Milne in 1857. An early barograph of theirs is shown in *Fig.* 191, made in 1876. It consists of an aneroid barometer and an eight-day pendulum clock, each with 8 inch dials; between these is placed, in a vertical position, the cylinder with the recording paper attached to it. The instrument is in a walnut case and there is a maximum and minimum thermometer below the cylinder.

A thermobarograph in an oak case made by Negretti & Zambra around 1890 is shown in *Fig.* 192. In addition to a barograph, this instrument has a thermograph mounted over the barograph which consists of a curved bi-metallic strip; the acuteness of the curve increases or decreases as the temperature rises and falls and this raises or lowers the pen arm which is attached by levers to the strip, thus leaving a visual record of all temperature changes. The barograph by Negretti & Zambra in *Fig.* 193 is very unusual as it has a two-week scale; the clockwork mechanism rotates the left-hand spool so that the chart completes a full circuit in two weeks.

Succeeding generations of both families of Negretti and Zambra were actively engaged in the affairs of the firm. When Henry Negretti died in 1879, a new partnership was formed between his son, H.P.J. Negretti and J.W. Zambra and his son, J.C. Zambra.

Fig. 191   Walnut self-recording barometer by Negretti & Zambra, London, 1876 (*Littlebury Antiques, Saffron Walden*).

Fig. 192   Thermobarograph in oak case by Negretti & Zambra, c.1890 (*Peter D. Bosson, Wilmslow*).

155

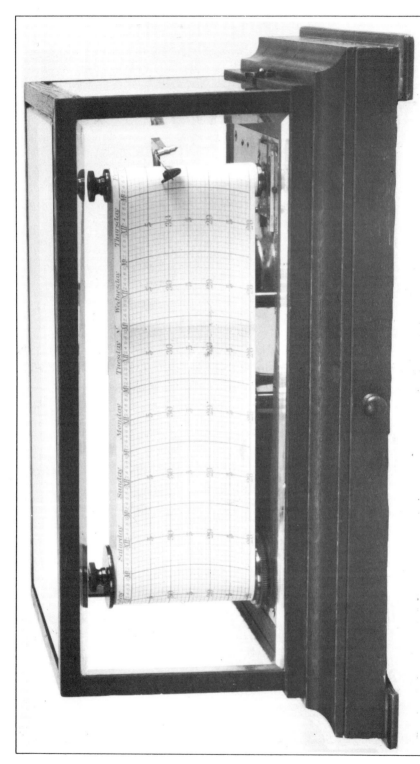

Fig. 193 Barograph with two-week scale by Negretti & Zambra, c.1900 (*Negretti Automation, Aylesbury*).

Joseph Warren Zambra retired in 1888 and M.W. Zambra joined his brother and Negretti in partnership. When J.C. Zambra died in 1892, H.P.J. Negretti and M.W. Zambra carried on the partnership until 1909, when M.W. Zambra retired. A new partnership was then formed between H.P.J. Negretti and his sons, Henry Noel and Paul Ernest with M.W. Zambra Jnr. H.P.J. Negretti died in 1919 and G. Zambra joined the other three in partnership. He retired in 1921. The remaining partners carried on until 1935 when M.W. Zambra Jnr retired, leaving H.N. and P.E. Negretti in partnership and ending the Zambra family link with the firm. Mark W. Zambra Jnr is remembered as a founder member and first President (in 1917) of the British Lampblown Scientific Glassware Manufacturers' Association. He was president of the Association for a total of 24 years and secretary for at least 14 years. In 1948 he was elected a life and honorary member in recognition of his long and valuable services; he died in 1952.

During the First World War, Negretti & Zambra's business was almost entirely engaged in work for the Ministry of Munitions on the production of various instruments. Two factories were also provided by the government during the Second World War at Chesterfield and Chobham for research and production of aircraft instruments and controls; some of their instruments were manufactured under licence in the United States of America.

In 1942 the sons of P.E. Negretti were admitted into partnership which continued until H.N. Negretti died in 1945. In 1946 the business was converted into a private company and into a public company in 1948. The company continued to expand, and in 1967 and 1976 it acquired companies making complementary instruments. However, the company itself was taken over in 1981 and became a subsidiary of Western Scientific Instruments Ltd. Following the acquisition, P.A. Negretti and P.N. Negretti, great grandsons of the founder Henry Negretti, stood down from the board and so severed the family links after 131 years. However, the name of Negretti continues as the business is still active today in Aylesbury under the name of Negretti Automation Ltd.

Conclusion

It is difficult to appreciate how hard-working and enterprising the early Italian migrants must have been, to arrive in a strange country and start up in business with only a very limited knowledge of the English language. They were obviously intelligent, resourceful and highly skilled men and were only hampered by their lack of fluency in the language to be able to participate fully in the life of English society. The majority married English women and by the end of the nineteenth century, although still proud of their Italian ancestry, were very much integrated into the life of the local community.

The Italians made a substantial contribution to scientific research by producing barometers and other scientific instruments which could more accurately measure air pressure and altitude. These were of great help to scientists, seamen, aviators, surveyors and others in the course of their work and research.

Their main influence was on the style and design of the mercury wheel barometer. They were responsible for introducing to Britain a completely new and very attractive design of wheel barometer which British makers were soon forced to copy. Their extant early barometers are of a very high quality and testify to the artistic ability and sense of style of the Italian makers. Early instruments, made between 1780 and 1860, now command very high prices and are sought after in the United Kingdom, on the Continent, in the United States of America and in Canada. Faithful reproductions of nineteenth-century Italian instruments are still being produced.

Index